The Art of Criticism;
as exemplified in
Dr. Johnson's Lives of
The Most Eminent
English Poets

Robert Potter

Garland Publishing, Inc., New York

1970

Bibliographical note:
this facsimile has been made from a
copy in the Yale University Library
(Im J637 T789).

Library of Congress Catalog Card Number: 75-112206

Printed in U.S.A.

THE ART OF CRITICISM.

THE

ART OF CRITICISM;

AS EXEMPLIFIED IN

DR. JOHNSON'S LIVES

OF

THE MOST EMINENT ENGLISH POETS.

—————————— *Ne fortè pudori*
Sit tibi Mufa Lyræ folers, et Cantor Apollo.

LONDON:

PRINTED FOR T. HOOKHAM, NEW BOND-STREET,

MDCCLXXXIX.

ART OF CRITICISM.

COWLEY.

ONE who pretends to give his opinion of such a work as the *Lives of the Poets*, ought to fancy himself qualified to prefix a somewhat satisfactory definition of genius. I therefore denominate it briefly,—*a mind vigorous, comprehensive, and indued with curiosity and susceptibility of impression.* Our author, near the beginning, teaches, that " the true genius is a mind of large and " general powers, accidentally determined " to some particular direction."

" The true genius is a mind of large and " general powers," would perhaps have

B   been

been a good diftinction ; but by what the. Doctor adds, he would fuppofe there is no natural bent of the mind ; which experience proves to be erroneous. Were it not, parents are right in difregarding the early indications of their children, whence to determine them to the moft fuitable occupations ; or rather, there are no fuch indications ; and much pleafantry has been ill beftowed on whipping pedagogues. But, in truth, the minds of men may be rather compared to lands, the kindlinefs of which for particular cropping is, farmers well know, to be regarded. On the other hand, the knowledge of fome things may be in almoft every mind, as fome plants thrive in almoft any foil.

On our author's hypothefis, Cicero might have been a Virgil ; Hogarth a Raphael ; and himfelf a Petrarch. He foon afterwards fays of wit,—

" Wit, like all other things fubject by
" their nature to the choice of man, has its
" changes and fafhions ; and at different
" times

" times takes different forms." Afterwards
he fays, " real mirth muſt be always na-
" tural, and nature is uniform."

Is not then the eſſence of wit, as well as
humour, uniform? Will not certain com-
binations of thought, always conſtitute one
as well as the other?

  " Do thou but threat."—— Cowley.

 " Every reader" (fays our author) " finds
" himſelf weary with this uſeleſs talk of an
" allegorical being."

Many have but an indifferent opinion of
the uſefulneſs of any poetry.

Putting this ſpeech in the mouth of *Envy*,
may perhaps be cenſurable in Epic proper ;
otherwiſe I think it beautiful, and the found
is wonderfully adapted to the ſenſe. In
" ſtill at thy *voice* ſtart,"—every ear, to
which the chinking of a guinea is not more
agreeable than ſterling verſe, will lay the
emphaſis on *voice* ; and many of Cowley's

lines fhould be fcanned in reading, like this in his Nemeæan Ode of Pindar,—

Black *blood*, and *fi'ry breath*, and pois'nous *foul* he *fqueezes out.*

Moreover, thofe who wifh to mafter Englifh verfification, fhould practice reading Cowleys, Shakefpeares, and Miltons.

Cowley is, on the whole, pourtrayed with ingenuity and penetration, and with juftice ; fo that indeed it is not eafy to add much to that which our author has faid of him.

DENHAM.

DENHAM.

THERE is a falfe concord in the fixth line of the quotation concerning tranflation : *flick* fhould be *flicks* ; *narrownefs,* not *arts,* being the correfpondent.

ʳ " Some hour propitious to poetry."—I hope our author will not contradict this hereafter. In the verfes on the Thames, *whofe gravel* would have been better.

MILTON.

" THE fpeed of the horfeman muft be " limited to the power of his " horfe." Yet fomewhat depends on the fkill of the rider.

" The celebrated word *Smectymnuus.*"— I am at a lofs to apprehend how the initial letters (of the names of fix perfons I fuppofe he means, if he means any thing,) could form a word of juft eleven.

" Such is the controverfial merriment of " Milton. His gloomy ferioufnefs is yet " more offenfive. Such is his malignity, " that hell grows darker at his frown." This is a dreadful relation, which our author was refolved fhould not fall fhort in hideoufnefs of its object.

Some pages after, we have *either* for *both.* " He was now poor and blind." A pertinent remark, which, together with the confideration

confideration of his fine genius, may account for the favour fhewn him by a monarch not deftitute of genius himfelf, whofe
right withal, like that of others to fove-
reignty, was originally founded on actions
little lefs dark than hell; fo that the affection for all great perfons whatfoever,
muft virtually and rationally depend on
their own deferts, not on thofe of their
tyrant-progenitors, to adore whom would
not be far from worfhiping the devil.

" All his wives were virgins." A pe-
remptory affertion truly.

" Minifterial," ufed in a double meaning unworthy of the author of a large dictionary.
" This dependance of the foul upon"
(why *upon?* would not *on* be fufficient?)
" the feafons ; thofe temporary and peri-
" odical ebbs and flows of intellect may, I
" fuppofe, juftly be derided as the fumes
" of vain imagination. *Sapiens dominabitur*
" *aftris ;*" — fed, *aftra regunt homines.* I
warned the Doctor not to contradict his

B 4   " hour

" hour propitious to poetry." Indeed I
do not affirm that he does fo here. However, experience, I apprehend, convinces
moft perfons of being affected by the feafons and weather, which is true to a pro-
verb. Alfo, why may not the moon influence genius as well as an ague? It is reafonable to fuppofe, that fuch a one as Milton's might fometimes flag. *Non femper ar-
cum tendit Apollo.* And it is not likely that
he fhould fancifully fuppofe himfelf infpired in the winter, and not in the beft
part of the year; he who was fo rapt with
vernal delight. A little after the Doctor
is undoubtedly right. Since a northern
ifland, Britain, has produced more genius
than all the world befides, fufficiently con-
futing the notion of geographical genius;
neverthelefs Dutchmen would do well to
apply themfelves rather to the culture of
cabbages.

" If lefs could be performed by the
" writer, lefs likewife would content the
" judges of his work."

It

It is the character of genius to grafp at perfection and univerfality. However, the Doctor at length ridicules his own criticifm with much candour, and draws his humour to a focus, by admitting that at all events the author of *Paradife Loft* might have been the rival of Tom Thumb, or a one-eyed mole; and that the copy might be worth a middling horfe. But it feems ftrange that his daughters fhould read feveral languages all day long without underftanding a word of any one,

" *L'Allegro & Il Penferofo.*"—It is amazing that from fingularity and caprice, the worthy Doctor fhould attack his whole fraternity of poets while he is writing their lives. He wifhed, one would think, to perfuade that he had a general averfion to nature. If he mentions love, it is to ridicule it; if the country, it is to ficken at it. Alas! Johnfon had no tafte for a garden, grove, or a fpring. *Speluncæ vivique lacus,* the darkling dell and the nightingale had no charms for him. To him the elements of poetry were uncongenial, and only excited his laughter.

laughter. According to one of his *Ramblers*, a fwept hearth, fire-pan and tongs were his infpirers; and if, perhaps, he did not prefer a marrow-bone, he delighted in wielding the cleaver of criticifm; and the fmoke of London was as pleafant to him as a coal-pit to a neighbour of Newcaftle. How different was his mafter! Is it poffible that the imitator of Addifon fhould be fonder of a fhining fender than a brook, and that the writer of the Englifh Dictionary fhould with the hand of burlefque, throw dirt at the *Penferofo*, at that which breathes the very foul of fimplicity? Metaphyfical wit was indeed ill calculated for Johnfon, who expected rather to make a found meal of a poem, than to quaff fpiritual nectar. Alas! the manner in which the Penferofo is ftripped of its colouring! As if a traveller fhould picture a fine palace by faying, that the floor of a chamber was taken from a rookery; a door brought from Jamaica; a wainfcot from Norway; and a painted window from an imperial monaftery.

Reciting a poem in fuch a detached manner,

ner, is like expecting a clock to strike when
taken to pieces ; is not analysing, but dislo-
cating. The *Allegro*, valuable as it is, is
necessarily inferior ; but is copied by a tasty
modern, the author of the *Bath-Guide*. In
the following pages, a good character is
given of Comus, which is then dismissed as
" inelegantly splendid, and tediously in-
" structive." We are wound up to a considerable pitch of expectation, and then, at
last, as Virgil and Homer raised founding
names with the intention of knocking their
owners at head,—hey! pass! 'tis gone!
On the contrary, after exerting his humour
on the *Penseroso* and *Allegro*, the Doctor
converts them into " two noble efforts of
" imagination." The reader is in the situa-
ation of James I. who, when he heard a
cause, was always of the opinion of the
counsel who spoke last. When Johnson is
at work on his fig-tree, it is impossible to
tell whether he will convert it to a god or
a chopping-block.

" I am now to examine *Paradise Lost* ;
" a poem, which, considered with respect
" to

" to defign, may claim the firft place ; and,
" with refpect to performance, the fecond,
" among the productions of the human
" mind."

In regard to this affertion, doubtlefs little
acceptable to the admirers of Virgil thus
denied competition ; it does not require
much penetration to difcover that, for defign, Johnfon places *Paradife Loft* before the
Iliad, and for performance, between that
and the Eneid ; the Odyffey, &c. being, I
prefume out of the queftion : that confequently *Paradife Loft* is fuperior or inferior
to the *Iliad*, as defign and performance are
to be comparatively rated. The reader,
neverthelefs, pondering whether, the ardu-
oufnefs of his fubject taken into the account,
Milton's performance, as well as defign, is
not equal to Homer's. Still perhaps we
fhould not haftily afcribe to Milton an ab-
folute preference, by reafon of the perhaps
accidental difadvantage of Homer, that
Milton's unparalled fubject was not within
the compafs of his choice, becaufe unknown
to him ; and becaufe Milton was his imitator

tator in outrageoufnefs. Perhaps indeed
the *Iliad* may be confidered as more the
offspring of the genuine rays of Phœbus,
Paradife Loft as an exotic product of the
hot-houfe; perhaps the former may claim
the palm of nature, the latter of art.

" Its perufal is a duty rather than a plea-
" fure. We read Milton for inftruction;
" retire haraffed and overburdened; and
" look elfewhere for recreation. We defert
" our mafter, and feek for companions."

It may be doubted whether this is panegyric or fatire; but it hardly correfponds
with the angelic war being the " favourite
" of children," which yet it is. It muft be
confeffed, that there are in *Paradife Loft*
many rugged paths between its fcenes of
grandeur and beauty. As to fchoolmafters,
of which ufeful fraternity was Milton, being
the butts of the world, the reafon is plain;
they being fure to run the gauntlet of their
fcholars for life, and to be repaid in wit for
birch; and to ridicule them more effectual-
ly, our language has confpired by affigning
them

them an odd appellation. When **Pipes had**
worn to pieces his love-letter, he is difpatched to a forry *pedagogue* to fupply him
with an elegant fuccedaneum.

Our author's obfervations on verfification
are fuch as difcover his dexterity in defence
of gingle. The reader will be pleafed with
Mrs. Montague's remark on blank verfe, in
her critique on Corneille's Cinna.—" Poffi-
" bly there is as much of difficulty in blank
" verfe to the poet (not, I think, to thofe
" converfant in it) as there appears of eafe
" in it to the reader. Like the ceftus of
" Venus, formed by the happy fkill of the
" graces, it beft exerts its charms, whilft
" the artifice of the texture is partly con-
" cealed. Dryden, who brought the art
" of rhyme to great excellence, endea-
" voured to introduce it on our ftage; but
" nature and tafte revolted againft an imi-
" tation of dialogue, fo entirely different
" from that in which men difcourfe.

" The verfe M. de Voltaire thus con-
" demns, is perhaps not lefs happily (bet-
" ter

" ter furely) adapted, than the iambic to
" the dramatic offices. It rifes gracefully
" into the fublime; it can flide happily in-
" to the familiar; haften its career if com-
" pelled by vehemence of paffion; paufe in
" the hefitation of doubt; appear lingering
" and languid, in dejection and forrow; is
" capable of varying its accent, and adapt-
" ing its harmony to the fentiment it fhould
" convey, and the paffion it would excite,
" with all the power of mufical expreffion."

This fine defcription, though a lady's, is
embaraffed with a pedantic fuperabundance
of comma's, which, multiplied, are often
productive of confufion inftead of clearnefs.
Mr. Mafon obferves, that dramatic, which
is colloquial verfe, muft efpecially have
paufes in the lines; and that in blank verfe
in general, " the harmony never refults
" from lines, but paffages; and thofe of
" very unequal extent."

Rhyme, in which Otway and Dryden
wrote tragedy, has, after I have been reading blank verfe, appeared to me trifling,
tink-

tinkling, and childish, like Latin rhymes, in other species of poetry as well as dramatic; and muft, I think, in every kind of writing have fuch an effect on manly ears accuftomed to the dignity of blank verfe, though a forbidding term. Highly prepofterous it certainly is, to jingle through paffion and defpair, horrors and death. Blank verfe is fufficiently out of the track of converfation; and though poetical profe, like that of *Telemachus*, is rather dull in the clofet; I cannot help thinking that, plays being intended for acting, not reading, it is habit that has confirmed the opinion that verfe of fome kind is neceffary to the ftage, and that admeafurement is indifpenfable to the *vis dramatica*. If, however, notwithftanding that, according to Horace, tragedy, for the moft part, complains in familiar language, goes on foot inftead of riding the great horfe; it is neverthelefs adjudged that verfe cannot be difpenfed with: ftill much of a tragedy might be in profaic, rifing occafionally into verfe when the fervour of paffion or of fentiment may be imagined to raife the foul to enthufiafm, and dictate numbers to the actor,

actor, as the writer might have been thus
affected, namely, thofe of blank verfe certainly more fluent and eafy than rhymes ;
the latter being, by Jofeph Warton, well
compared to latin hexameter and pentame-
ter, which are indeed adapted to love fongs,
Cupid, and childifhnefs. Johnfon had the
perfpicacity to perceive that rhymes are
fitted to didactic terfenefs, for which alone
he was qualified, and therefore wifely al-
leges all that can be faid in favour of it, as
he does alfo of Pope's modernization of
Homer. Compared with the learned claf-
fical Jofeph Warton, Johnfon has, together
with affectation and rhodomontade, more
fhrewdnefs and poignancy, but ufually lefs
tafte and candour ; their fentiments fometimes agreeing, but being as often different
and oppofite. Of the mud caft by Johnfon,
as related by Bofwell, on Mrs. Montague's
book, the true motive was probably her neglect of him, his favage manners not fuit-
ing her groupe of literati. As *Telemachus*
in general, and many parts of the *Arcadia,*
and of the *Scriptures*, may be properly ftiled
poetic profe, perhaps Bifhop Lowth's verfion

C   of

of *Ifaiah* may be properly denominated *profaic poetry.*

Our author, cynical as he was, waved, in pafling final fentence on Milton's epic, his fneering, and even a due reprehenfion of *Paradife Loft*, which is very faulty in the converfion of all things to the purpofe of poetical embellifhment, whereby he has conftituted a huge chaotic romance.

It is true that in the Old Teftament, the chariots, arrows, fhield, &c. of the Almighty, are figuratively fpoken of; but it is cafually. The Mefliah and the angels are not reprefented as battling with fwords, fpears, mufquets, and cannon, united with all the extravagance of Homer's fighting mythology, whilft Satan is fometimes defcribed in fuch a manner, his prowefs is fo mighty, and his armour fo brilliant, as to tend to excite admiration inftead of horror. Again, as to theology; Milton is any thing or nothing; Trinitarian, Arian, Socinian, or neither, as fuited his poetry; and I know not but he would have been Mahometan,

Mahometan, or Diabolian, had Cromwell, the devil's fecretary, Milton being under-fecretary, commanded it : therefore the inftruction we look for in *Paradife Loft*, can hardly be eminent refpecting the faith of this great mafter.

Pope has an infamous couplet, wherein, for the fake of his poetry, he paffes an indirect panegyric on the apoftate angels,—

" Ambition firft fprung from your blefs'd abodes ;
" The glorious fault of angels and of gods."

Milton was no lefs unequal than Cowley; his verfions of fome pfalms being in the true ftile of Sternhold and Hopkins, and inferior to Bacon's; and the concluding line in particular of the fonnet on his wife, is in the Cowleian ftile of wit.

C 2   BUTLER.

BUTLER.

" Omnia vult belle Matho dicere; dic aliquando
" Et bene, dic neutrum, dic aliquando male."

ADDISON indeed obferves, that Milton
knew the art of relieving the reader at
intervals, in order to unbend his mind to
come frefh to his principal fubject; but authors are rarely commended for the eafy at-
tainment of writing ill; and Johnfon, I believe, would have hardly acknowledged that
ever he did, how true foever a confeffion: he
who would be always in the right. Some
critics have taken great pains to excufe Homer's naps, but have not endeavoured to
raife merit from them; yet fuch an alle-
gation is a very convenient apology at leaft.

" Imagination is ufelefs without know-
" ledge," is fo far true, that perfons in that
predicament are poorly qualified to benefit others; but their minds are happily
qualified for the reception of entertainment.
" Nor,

" Nor, even though another Butler
" fhould arife, would another *Hudibras* ob-
" tain the fame regard." But, according
to our author's own theory, true general
humour muft always entertain ; and fomewhat of general humour is neceffarily blended with particular ; fo that Cervantes, Butler, Anftey, Peter Pindar, and others, will
be always read with pleafure. But burlefque, the grand fource of ridicule, is of
a nature lefs truly engaging, and will be
confequently lefs permanently prevalent
when ludicrous than when grave; which
latter kind of humour is rather a curious
delineation of the foibles and manners of
others, than any laughable reprefentation.

C 3   OTWAY.

OTWAY,

AS to the affinity between writing and acting plays, one principally depends on mental, the other on corporeal accomplifhments. The Irene of our author, who would not have excelled in the latter, has fome inaccuracies, and too much of the horrible. Even tragedies are exhibited as entertainments; and who can be gratified with the reprefentation of tortures? It is the excitement of contemplative pity, of the fentimental and fpiritual affections, the terrific and alarming; like the cataftrophe of the *Duke of Guife*, and of the magic of inventive and eccentric genius exhibited in the matchlefs hints of Shakefpeare, that carrying us away from earth, are the beft calculated for the drama, whatever is the verbal import of *tragedy*, rather than things excruciating and fhocking to behold. It was probably to Shakefpeare's ethereal imagination, that Milton, who, if allowed to be the greater poet, ought, to balance their

deferts,

deferts, to refign the palm of genius, was indebted for his exquifitenefs, and Pope for the manners of his Sylphs. In the *Tempeſt*, do we not acknowledge the fountain whence flowed the living fpring of the *Penſeroſo*, and perceive the machinery of the *Rape of the Lock?* If Shakeſpeare, how childiſh fo-ever are Proſpero's threats to Ariel, had not written

> " Sea-nymphs hourly ring his knell.
> " Hark! now I hear them—Ding—dong—bell."

which itſelf, had it been by an ordinary writer tranſlated from Ovid, or written by Cowley, would, I fuſpect, have been deem-ed childiſh. Indeed, as extremes in a man-ner meet, fo do reaches and childiſhneſs of thought. If, I fay, Shakeſpeare had not written theſe fancifully charming lines, would Milton have written

> " Over fome wide-water'd ſhore,
> " Swinging flow with fullen roar?"

Yet were they inhabited by twin fouls, one of which might only anticipate the other. But if Milton drew from Shakeſpeare's fount, evident it is that Shakeſpeare him-

ſelf

felf drew from a ftill higher head, and wa-
tered the enchanting exotics of the *Tempeft*
from the celeftial rivers of the Helicon of
the *Apocalypfe* ; witnefs thefe lines, &c.

" Sometimes a thoufand twanging inftruments
" Will hum about mine ears, and fometimes voices*."

By the way, how abfurd is Pope's affigning the guidance of the planets to fuch
puny agents as the Sylphs.

Otway's life is an imperfect epigram, becaufe too long.

---

* Revelation, chap. VIII. v. 5. chap. XIV .v. 2. &c.

WALLER.

WALLER.

THE writer of the life prefixed to
" his works." Why would not our
author tell us who this was in one word,
inftead of employing nine, to leave us in
the dark? The frequent occurrence of
thefe blind periphrafes, is an objection to
thefe *lives*, fimilar to that which he makes to
the epitaphs of Pope without the names,
for though every one of the prefent age
knows the perfons meant, that may not be
the cafe with pofterity.

" *Sachariffa*, from the Latin appellation
" of *fugar*." Sugar is faid to be an acid;
and Waller's fugar had undergone digeftion.

" He doubtlefs praifed many whom he
" would have been afraid to marry; and
" perhaps married one whom he would
" have been afhamed to praife."

Such

Such ſtrokes as theſe, how juſt ſoever is
this in reſpect to truth, and how taſteful
itſelf to the claſſical cenſures of antitheſis,
who doat on the pure ſimplicity of the ancients, diſcriminate a writer of genius and
enliven a ſubject. Antitheſes, eſpecially in
rhyme, preſent themſelves at once to the
mind, like a regular building. Mallet, in
his life of Bacon, has ſome ſuch ſtrokes.
Voltaire abounds with them, delighting
eſpecially to level them at prieſts, whoſe
aſſiſtance he is neverthelefs ſaid to have
craved when ſick, though I can hardly believe him to have been ſo weak as to reſt
his ſalvation on a ſuborned repentance in
the lap of men, who, like indeed other reli-
gioniſts, devote their faces to God, and
hearts to the devil; and, a few members excepted, ought to be hooted out of the
world for their villainous hypocriſy, and
will doubtleſs bring the grey hairs of the
church with ſorrow to the grave; wretches,
whoſe trade it is to barter inheritances in
the other world by auction. If that ſpright-
ly author was deiſtical, I hope it cannot
be truly affirmed that he was atheiſtical.

If

If his *candide* feems to bear hard on the goodnefs of Providence, it may be attributed to the reverberation of extremes propagated by others, and to his impatience of Pope's fatalifm, differing from that of others in imputing the diforders of the world to the Subreme Being; whereas other fatalifts annul his providence, by fubftituting nature in its place; but each fyftem alike cuts up morality and virtue by the roots. *Whatever is, is right*, without qualification, is directly contradictory to the fact that evil ever entered the world at all, and of which truth nobody was more fenfible than Pope himfelf, who was fo fond of dealing out the appellations of knave and villain, words, I apprehend, without meaning, if *wrong* had never been committed: fo that the axiom renders Johnfon's culpable reprefentation of Pope's epiftolary fatires, that he could not hope to mend the world, true indeed, as it could want no mending. Neverthelefs, every perfon of found piety and religion hopes and believes, that through the controuling providence of God, which faid to the fea, *Thus*

far

far fhalt thou go, and no farther, all diforders
will be at length rectified, and that *all will
finally be right*.   Indeed Johnfon's morality,
interfperfed through his biography, is of an
indifferent, vulgar, worldly, and warped
into a fufpicious caft, that feemed to con-
fute Pope's pofition.   But indeed, as fays
Shakefpeare's Timon, thofe who haftily
blame perfons for being captivated with the
blandifhments of pleafure, are fuch as never experienced it.   So it may be alleged,
that Johnfon wrote his rigid precepts of
morality, when a bulk, not a fopha, was
his feat of reft : that he had been " a flave,
" whom Fortune's tender art with fa-
" vour never clafped."   For as adverfity
is excellently denominated a fchool, fo is
profperity a fnare.   However, a man of
his underftanding fhould, at all times, have
referved *amo meliora* for an apology, and not
have left the Heathen Stoics, men who, on
account of their felf-denial, deferve the appellation of natural Chriftians, the palm of
moral philofophy.

Of paradoxes, the former part of the
twenty-

twenty-fecond verfe of the third chapter of
Genefis;—*And the Lord God faid, behold the
man* (the woman is not mentioned) *is become as one of us, to know good and evil*—
feems to prefent one. Yet may it not be
refolved in this manner?—That before their
fall, Adam and Eve knew not, were unacquainted with the mixed condition enfuing
to the world, having experienced nothing
but good, unfophifticated with evil. As to
the latter part of this verfe, *and now left he
put forth his hand, and take alfo of the tree of
life, and eat, and live for ever,* it is beyond my
refolution; for to interpret it that mankind, how brutal foever they are, and *like the
beafts that perifh*, will not be immortal; or
that the wicked will not be fo, though a
feemingly defirable thing, and *that many are
called, but few are chofen*, with fome few
other texts, are to be underftood in fuch a
fenfe, feems rafh and heterodox. And that
Mrs. Piozzi, in her expreffion, that our author's excellence was beyond that of perifh-
able beings, alluded to that of Scripture,
like the beafts that perifh, is a prefumption
ftill lefs juftifiable. I may here obferve,
that

that one Francis Ofborn, has a curious remark on the words, *The feed of the woman
fhall bruife the ferpent's head* ;—that the meaning might be, that he who fhould do it,
would be born of a woman only.

 " They (fays Waller) who think them-
" felves in danger, and they who have no-
" thing left, can never give freely," feems,
in the latter part, defective ; the tenour
feeming to require, *they who have nothing
left, are never afraid of giving freely.*

 " Coufin Waller, I muft talk to thofe
" men in their own way," fhews Cromwell
in his true colours,—that of a villainous hypocrite, which fome perfons have endeavoured to difguife, as if he thought himfelf, or at length perfuaded himfelf, that
he was fincere in his affectation of piety,
making, as fays *Profpero, in the Tempeft,* " a
" liar of his memory. Religious cant confifts in vefting common modern ideas in antiquated fcriptural phrafeology ; in chang-
ing the effence and unaffected fpirit of religion, into fenfelefs words and prepofterous
fentences,

sentences, like affected distinctions of square-
toed shoes, multiplicity of buttons and long
pockets, and is burlesque and mockery. Of
the engines of tyranny, there is none more
efficacious and grating than creating laws
to restrain others, and to be dispensed with
by the enactors. And this glaring policy
it was that critically framed *the self-denying
ordinance*, pretended to restrain members of
Parliament from holding commissions in the
army under the cloak of patriotism, which
Cromwell himself was notoriously to break
through, seize the very command of the
army after having virtually commanded it
already, murder garrisons, and trample on
the nation. Yet, because mankind are always to be fools, a wise axiom of Pope,
we have lately seen triumphant, hypocritical patriotism as preposterously impudent
as Cromwell's, holden out in the practices
concerning the Irish commercial treaty,
which was respectively represented as injurious to both kingdoms, and both were
fools enough to gulp down the matchless
paradox hewn out with a cleaver, so coarsely
as to have stuck in the throat of any other
people

people on earth; the offspring of which is
fuch an headlefs monfter as the world has
never before feen, and as cannot poffibly
live long; but will probably, e'er it die,
difgorge, like the dragon in the Revelation,
a deluge that will fhake one or other of
the kingdoms to the foundation. If ap-
pearances may be depended on, the monarch of France alfo may experience the
fruits of paradoxes, and fee duplicity
brought home to his own door; fo dangerous it is to fofter a ferpent, dandle fire,
and raife the devil in fport. Neverthelefs,
if he was outwitted by the fanatics of Ame-
rica, his conceffions to the Proteftants will
ftamp him the real patriot of mankind.

Our author mentions Cromwell with a
moderation that I fhould not have expected.
It may indeed be alleged, according to Mr.
Bofwell, that it is of little importance of
what tyrant-conqueror the fuceffors bear
fway; and that the nation, in acquiefcing
in Oliver's ufurpation, of evils chofe the
leaft. But of thefe evils this arch hypocrite
has been the principal caufe, who had regularly

gularly conducted things to such a situation, that the nation was obliged either to admit a notorious usurpation, or be plunged into utter confusion and ruin. Cromwell seems to have surpassed Cæsar, in that, as Warburton observes, the spirit of the nation was at the highest when he subdued it; whereas Rome was enervated with luxury; and there had been a perpetual dictator before.

By the way, Sylla's resignation, his character considered, seems one of the most extraordinary events in history; and to have designated him ambitious and savage, two qualities usually united, as he had been the greatest, because the wisest man of the three, exhibits a mighty proof of the vanity of all human things; and that on the mind, even the love of power, the last infirmity of greater minds, though the greatest of all are superior still, unless indeed for the opportunity of doing good. But the underminers of states may be necessitated to persist, from the danger or impossibility of retreating. Those possess not the most

D   exalted

exalted ideas who cannot really believe, that cannot be perfuaded that Diogenes preferred his tub, whence he might expatiate on the orbs of heaven, to the throne, tottering, whereon Alexander furveyed the fubject earth.

Cromwell affected by diffimulation that which Cæfar accomplifhed by largefs; and may perhaps be confidered as a cunninger politician than the other. In public and private courage and conduct, they were equal and wonderful: but Cromwell had nothing but fly art, to oppofe to Cæfar's oratory and literature. Farther; Cæfar was liberal; Cromwell was mean; and would not at a lefs propitious time have rifen higher than a methodift parfon. Cæfar collected diffipation into monarchy; Cromwell debafed monarchy into tyranny.—— Their ambition and narrow failure of a crown, had a very remarkable affinity; and perhaps after all, they both deferve the name of cowards, for ftanding fhilly fhally within reach of that for which their fouls longed. There was alfo another refemblance in their warfare: that had Pompey's pey's army had patience, Cæsar would probably have been ruined ; and that had not the Scotch army of faints been induced by fecond fight to engage Cromwell, he would probably have been reduced by famine.

On the rebellion, Francis Ofborn remarks, that the Jefuits, always working by indirect methods, landed it in Prefbyterian bottoms, and in thofe of the Anabaptifts; who naturally, he fays, difapprove of all government whatfoever. And he obferves in the another place, that the Arminians are to Papifts, juft what fcallions are to onions; that is, they are only not quite fo ftrong. As to the Puritans, though candour fhould be always embraced, it muft be acknowledged, that they joined with the Papifts in the time of James II. fo that even the moft incongruous extremes coincided in the intention of overturning the golden medium of the church of England. So excellent indeed is the medium in all things, though nothing on earth will be ever free from imperfection, that, corrupt and perverfe as is the lot of humanity, even reli-

D 2   gion

gion itfelf muft not be carried to extremes,
In fact, common fenfe, and the light of nature, have never been totally obfcured by religion and prieftcraft, which, by fuperftition, monaftic monopolization, &c. has even
threatened the extirpation of mankind.
For, among the manifold contrivances of
Providence, He has fo conftituted things,
that evils deftroy themfelves; and, when
outrageous, become their own cure; defpots
who have laid wafte the world, a Cæfar,
and a Kouli Khan, at length fell by a bod-
kin. Again, when knavery is univerfal,
fuch a fyftem is in a manner the fame with
univerfal honefty; becaufe all cheating, one
another in their turns, has a fimilar effect to
nobodys' cheating. When the Jewifh priefts
were fo numerous that all were about to
become priefts, as all people are now becoming Jefuits, a reform became abfolutely
neceffary, and defired by the priefthood itfelf. As the effect of all being priefts, (the
remark may be extended alfo to other
trades,) befides the impoverifhment of the
priefthood, and its virtual annihilation, there
being no ponds in the fea, muft be that of
depopulating

depopulating and laying wafte the world. Moreover, an overgrown, aged priefthocd and myftery, are in danger of letting in the light through their chinks, and enable the laity to get a glimpfe of the penetralia ; whereby, becoming witneffes of fome chicanery, they may erroneoufly conclude of the fubftance of religion itfelf, and fo perhaps indeed pafs from fuperftition to the meeting extreme of fcepticifm and irreligion ; the circumftance that renders the inculcation of hard myftery fo dangerous. And thus, in regard to evils undoing themfelves ; when tyranny, or chicanery of any kind, have threatened total defiruction, the elaftic *vis infita* inherent, notwithftanding its bafenefs, in human nature, buoying up in ftrong minds, has always availed more or lefs to pierce the veil drawn over the eyes of the fimple bulk of mankind, and fanned a fpark both of political and fpiritual liberty, and preferved from annihilation the human race ; an event, I will not however pronounce on, whether to be deprecated or wifhed. It is the natural confequence of infufferable oppreffion, notwithftanding the unprincipled

carelelfnefs,

careleſſneſs, cowardice, and ſelfiſhneſs of
mankind; that the pent tide of the people
forced upon its banks, ruſhes over and bears
down all before it. When the blood is driven
on the heart by deſpair, the heart muſt repel it, or death enſues. Says Oſborn, " keep
" reaſon always in your eye, which ſhould
" never be loſt ſight of in any worldly ac-
" tion, and be but eclipſed in things relat-
" ing to religion." He has withal a very
ſarcaſtic ſtroke at the Pope; " whoſe in-
" fallible holineſs, (ſays he,) has announced
" himſelf a fool on record, in puniſhing
" Galileo for aſſerting the truth of there
" being antipodes."

" His (Waller's) opinion concerning the
" duty of a poet, is contained in this de-
" claration, — that he would blot from
" his works any line that did not contain
" ſome motive to virtue." And his motto
is

Non ego mordaci diſtrinxi carmine quenquam.

Perhaps it is not eaſy to conceive, how
love-verſes ſhould, in every line, inculcate
virtue

virtue in its common acceptation. Poffibly, as *virtus* imports *valour*, fo, by virtue, Waller might mean gallantry in love. This gallantry is, it feems, Gothic, which gives me an opportunity of noticing this paffage of this Ofborn, who was one of the queer dogs:—" If any lady be furioufly enamour-
" ed of you, whofe fortune cannot corre-
" fpond for the troubles incident to mar-
" riage, (which, God knows, are not a few),
" venture the lofs of her rather than your-
" felf: it being the higheft degree of folly
" to hang an indiffolvable padlock on your
" future hopes, only to fave a wenches'
" longing." He relates, that when King James I. partook of a huge treat made for him by Sir John Fortefcue, " his Majefty
" made a jeft of it, and departing, let a f—
" in the porch." Pardon me, reader.

The moft frequent objection to Waller's verfification is, not only ufing *do*, but accenting it: otherwife both *do* and *ed* need not be excluded diverfified poetry. His verfe is rather fmooth than vigorous:—

D 4   " Waller

" Waller was fmooth ; but Dryden taught to Join
" The varying paufe, the full-refounding line,
" The long majeftic march, and energy divine."

As to facred poetry, mine, and our author's
opinion, not coinciding, his idea of poetry
that it is ufelefs and improper for thofe
purpofes wh.ch are alone worthy of high
regard, having been engendered by fuperftition, I fhall pafs to a ftricture on the expreffion, *paffed the zenith*, which I think not
apt. The allufion is to noon. *Zenith* con-
veys a true idea of *height*, therefore the
zenith of glory is well, but does not with fo
much propriety defignate a ftage of the
progreffion of life. The variation of the
zenith is the fame, day and night, during
the twenty-four hours, fometimes indeed
called the day ; but compared with a man's
life, it is beft confidered as the time only
the fun is above the horrizon, or at moft,
from the break of day till its clofe ; the different points of the day's revolution corre-
fponding with the ftages of life. Be that
as it may, Fenton's allowance of only twenty
years of maturity to man's life, efpecially
applied

applied to Waller who wrote well till eighty-two, feems too fmall.

After an effort of exalted ftile refpecting religion,—" fuch as it is, it is known already," is a fall off not very intelligible.

Having noticed feveral obfervations of Mr. Francis Ofborn, I fhall take this opportunity of the mention of religion, to quote from him fomething of importance, the following prefumptions of the exiftence of a Deity:—" Nor are we" (as to ourfelves, in regard to the fphere of our own underftandings) " totally deftitute of a fha-
" dow of Omnifciency, fince, from a far lower
" fituation than heaven, we are able, at one
" glance to overlook a whole city, and by
" a fingle trumpet to alarum an army. Yet
" our fenfes are capable to receive no fmall
" augmentation from the affiftance of art.
" An infallible argument that the perfec-
" tion of thefe qualities does not determine
" in the perfon of any creature ; but is
" fomething paramount to all that hath yet
" rifen within the compafs of our experi-
                              " ence,

" ence, it being impoffible but that a fu-
" perlative power fhould reft fomewhere.
" Nor can we be competent judges of the
" motions of God, that have nothing to
" meafure by but fenfe, much too weak to
" difcern the motion of a fhadow, or the
" growth of a plant, till time hath rendered
" them apparent. Wherefore, we are far
" unable to comprehend the lines of Provi-
" dence, imperceptible to every intelligence
" but that of Him who has the fole difpo-
" fure of all things ; it not being probable
" that man fhould comprehend the out-
" goings of God, whilft he is unable to give
" any reafon for his own." And thus (he
might have added) whilft according to the
doleful ditty, " As in beginning was, is
" now, and fo fhall be for evermore." We
dream that the world and things will always continue in their prefent ftate, and
fools and knaves hope it alfo : we may fuddenly find the day of judgment at our doors,
as a thief in the night.

Waller, whofe *life* is written with ability
and impartiality, feems to have deferved
the

the title of a Vicar of Bray. And let me defend our author againſt the cenſure of mixing politics with literature ; though not of varniſhing over King Charles's illegal meaſures ; I think with Hume, that ſome-thing may be juſtly alleged for them. Nor, on the other hand, of frittering away thoſe of the dregs of the faction. A biographer was profeſſedly to write an account of the the lives of the poets, and conſequently of their circumſtances and characters.

But I think he has made rather a jumble, by giving a partial account of their writ-ings, in the courſe of their lives ; and that the work would have been more perfect, if, in proceeding with their hiſtories, he had only mentioned the titles and dates of their writings, and reſerved his critiques by them-ſelves.

POMFRET.

POMFRET.

OF this placid poet, who is difpatched laconically, the lines that moft pleafed me were thefe on pleafing melancholy ;—

" The fweeteft mufic to the grove we owe,
" Is mournful Philomel's melodious woe."

DORSET.

DORSET.

THE adage, that *the elder brother has the estate, and the younger the sense*, is not well founded. That the younger should have most learning, and the elder most genius, might be expected; but both seems accidental. It is indeed very meritorious in persons born to opulence, to be at the pains of acquiring knowledge. For young persons qualified by fortune and genius for merriment and conviviality, to leave the flowery paths of sense for the thorny ones of science; to quit, in spite of the taunts of the gay and the amorous, the flowing bowl for Coke and Lyttelton, and the smiles of beauty for triangles and parallelograms, seems almost marvellous; yet constellations of literary nobles, as Roscommon, Hallifax, Sheffield, Dorset, &c. have appeared.

JOHN

JOHN PHILIPS.

WE underſtand that Philips preſents us with the huſks, but makes an apology for the kernels of poetry: that in his *Blenheim* we find the lumber and dim windows, but not the magnificence and good cheer of ancient caſtles; that we view the quarries of ſtones and dwarfs, but look in vain for the giants and enchantments of Shakeſpeare and Milton: that, according to Swift's caricature of Dryden compared with Pindar, we have an enormous helmet to contemplate, in which the head is almoſt loft. It is not to be doubted, that critics pick up many of their notices from converſation, &c. ſtill they muſt not be deprived of the merit of them; and Johnſon's criticiſm, though ſevere, on John Philips, has rarely appeared to advantage. The *Splendid Shilling* is a very pleaſing burleſque of the beſt, that is the grave kind, conſiſting in the inveſtiture of trifling ſubjects in pompous ſtile; the other, the putting off a

sublime

fublime fubject in·mean ftile, that is the ludicrous kind, being inferior. Miller's criticifm, that the poem on cyder is really inftructive in the art, though I apprehend
King's, if it was King's, poetical receipt to
make an apple-pye to be a more practical
treatife ; reminds me of the fame queftion
concerning Virgil's *Georgics*, which, even in
England, I think not a ufelefs treatife on
agriculture, if well underftood even now
when the fcience is in fo improved a ftate ;
but I am entirely at a lofs to underftand
Virgil's caution not to fow wheat before
May, (Georg. I. 1. 225.) if *Maiæ* means
May, left the ears fhould be empty ; an
idea that, were the fpring the time of fow-
ing wheat in Italy, which, however, feems
from the context not to have been the cafe,
contradicts all experience, late-fown corn
producing the thinneft and worft grain.

WALSH:

WALSH.

IF it is confidered that this poet was a gallant, and attached to Gothic affections, he finds more quarter than might have been expected; but at laft receives this kick,— " He is known more by his familiarity " with great men, than by any thing done " or written by himfelf."

It is, however, probable from that very circumftance, that he had fomething in him engaging; unlefs drinking and gaming, &c. were the accomplifhments that in thofe days obtained the notice of the great.

As our author ends his firft volume like a Parthian, we fhall fee him enter on the fecond like a crab; I mean his Latin idiom of beginning a fentence at the latter end, with *of*, as at the commencement cf the life of Dryden.

DRYDEN.

DRYDEN.

" **An** horrid ftillnefs firft invades the ear."

" **D**EATH is alfo privation; yet who
" has made any difficulty of affign-
" ing to death a dart, and the power of
" ftriking?"

Wretched quibbling and contradiction
this, for contradiction-fake! Death is indeed reprefented as an allegorical perfon in
fcripture, &c. fome kinds of which very
juftly give an idea of ftriking; but a ne-
gation of founds invading the ear is mere
nonfenfe in terms, like *lucus a non lucendo.*

" No grain of fenfe does in one line appear,
" Thy words big bulks of boift'rous bombaft bear.
" With noife they move, and from play'rs mouths rebound,
" When their tongues dance to thy words' empty found.
" By thee infpir'd the rumbling verfes roll,
" As if that rhyme and bombaft lent a foul.

As Dryden's outrageous effufions, however mixed up with indigefted nonfenfe and

E

puns,

puns, could not but have value; fo we have here an excellent defcription of bombaft, and afterwards another vigorous fpecimen of indignant fatire;—

" From breaths of fools thy commendation fpreads ;
" Fame fings thy praife with mouths of loggerheads ;
" With noife and laughing each thy fuftian greets,
" 'Tis clapt by quires of empty-headed cits."

In which we perceive that coarfe expref-fions, fuch as Juvenal adopted, are thofe for hacking and hewing, for which a cleaver is much better fitted than a polifhed inftru-ment.

" This, as Lamotte relates himfelf to " have heard, was the real practice of the " poet."

This is an odd relation, that Dryden fhould think a fit of the gripes neceffary to defcribe a hero in love. Indeed a meta-phyfician, or a methodift, might benefit the fpirit by purging off the grofs parts. Soon after we find our author calling his father an old bookfeller. He was hardly always old ;—

old ;—though perfons have been faid to have been born drunk.

" —As to retire for quiet to an infallible
" church.'

This is a fentence worthy at leaft of as wife a theologian as our author, who him-felf was always old and antiquated in reli-gious matters. An *infallible church* that (he might have added) annihilates concern and thought, and which is the fifter of a kind of inverfe fcepticifm that is to lead men blindfold to heaven. As to what he adds, that every artifice was then ufed to fhew Popery in its faireft form ; were the Pro-teftants (probably three fourths of the na-tion) idle, and did they not fhew her in her fouleft form ? " It is natural to hope, " that a comprehenfive, is likewife an ele- " vated foul ; and that whoever is wife, is " alfo honeft." By *wife*, is meant *knowing* ; for, doubtlefs, every *wife* man, in the true fenfe of the word, is honeft; *rogue and fool*, notwithftanding the large portion of the

E 2   world

world comprehended in thofe terms, being certainly fynonimous.

" In this volume is comprifed the well-
" known Ode on St. Cecilia's Day, which,
" as appeared by a letter communicated to
" Dr. Birch, he fpent a fortnight in com-
" pofing and correcting." Dr. Warton,
I think, fays that he wrote it at one fitting:
ftill, the correction included, both accounts
may be true, though Dryden was not wont
to revife, and the piece is not correct.

As to the colloquial dullnefs of Dryden,
who wrote fo freely and carelefsly, and was
agreeable to the great, his modefty might
embarafs his converfation: but it is not im-
probable, that he thought it beneath his
dignity to open in common company. If
we may believe Lord Chefterfield, the Duke
of Ormond was the moft innoffenfive and
weakeft of men; an account probably exaggerated.

The expreffion, *holy butcher*, however ridiculous,

diculous, is a good burlefque appellation for
the operators of barbarous and idiot fuperftition, in the execution of which, *ipfa pul-
cherrima, Dido* held the bowl; and Cicero,
of whom, with all his celebrity, it is dubi-
ous whether vanity or fuperftition rendered
him the greater fool, was as contemptible
as any one. If Dryden and Johnfon alfo
were poffeffed of fuperftition, it was not of
a fanguinary caft, though both of them
were poffeffed of a degree of favagenefs;
nor ought we to pronounce the original un-
corrected tenets of the Church of Rome erroneous. Indeed Dryden and Johnfon had
fome confiderable refemblances; and the ful-
tan Johnfon fignified from his chair in the ifle
of Sky, his project of keeping a feraglio) or
a harem, we fhould rather fay) with no lefs
dignity than the monarch Dryden iffued edicts
from his feat in the balcony at Will's. *But
there is no reafon for fuppofing that Johnfon difbelieved the religion which he only enter-
tertained thoughts of difobeying. He forgot his
duty rather than difowned it. His tendency to
being a Turk was the effect of levity, negligence,
and loofe converfation, with a defire of accom-*

E 3   *modating*

*modating himself to the corruption of the times,
by venturing to be wicked as far as he durst.
When he professed himself a convert to Mahome-
tanism, he did not pretend to have received any
new conviction of fundamental doctrines.* I
hope the reader will excuse this paraphrase
of the Doctor's apology for Dryden.

Three hundred verses for 12,000l. is just
sixpence a verse; which, according to the
present rate of money, would be, I suppose,
somewhat more than a shilling ; and the 20l.
which Milton was to receive first and last
for *Paradise Lost,* would be now perhaps
80l.

" *It was more eligible to go wrong with one
" than right with the other,"* is surely a dangerous apophthegm, somewhat resembling
the theological position, that men ought to
speak alike, whatever they think.

" To write *con amore,* with fondness for
" the employment, with perpetual touches
" and retouches, with unwillingness to take
" leave

" leave of his own idea, and an unwearied
" purſuit of unattainable perfection."

Certainly not. Yet of moſt writers, a
pocket-volume, in a cloſe ſtile and compact-
ed thought, is, in the preſent oppreſſion of
books, much preferable to a folio. If one's
firſt thoughts are the beſt, it is by chance ;
and they are like a lucky throw at dice ;
and he who depends on them for his reputation, will probably looſe it. The mind,
like a hampered net, is ſeldom at once diſ-
entangled ; beſides that the expreſſion is
nearly always improvable,

" He could not, like Milton and Cowley,
" have made his name illuſtrious merely
" for his learning."

It was hardly poſſible for a man continually ſcribbling, to dive into the depths of
ſcience. But indeed it is difficult to collect
from our author, whether Dryden was
learned or not. He ſeems to allow him an
intuitive knowledge ; a wide range, though
he kept the high road : repreſents his li-

terature,

terature, as either obvious, fuperficial, or
erroneous; as knowing things, but not
books; as hatching the egg without fitting
on it.

" More examples of more modes of com-
" pofition" is aukwardly expreffed.

" A tranflator is to be like his author;
"'it is not his bufinefs to excel him."

This affertion feems hypothetical. As a
tranflator will never equal fome beauties,
fhould he not compenfate by foftening fome
blemifhes? Pope, however cunningly our
author wards off the objection, may perhaps be juftly blamed for refining on Homer's fimplicity. Be that as it may, he,
quality and quantity taken together, is
probably the beft tranflator that ever
exifted. On Ovid's *Sappho to Phaon*, he has
efpecially much improved in the pathetic,
in which he alfo much excelled his mafter
Dryden, and has avoided fome puerilities.
Addifon, in his excellent fpecimens of the
Metamorphofes, conforms to the turn both

of

of the thought and poetry, his Englifh
dancing to the Latin.

" Allegories drawn to great length will
" always break. Charles could not run
" continually parallel with David."

Might it not hence be concluded, that
David or Charles were perfonifications?
Is the poem of *Abfalom and Achitophel* pro-
perly an allegory, and not rather a parallel?
Yet it cannot be eafily fuppofed that our
author did not know what an allegory is.

" The fubject had likewife another in-
" convenience: it admitted little imagery
" or defcription; and a long poem of mere
" fentiment *eafily* becomes tedious; though
" all the parts forcible, and every line kindles
" new rapture, the reader, if not relieved
" by the interpofition of fomething that
" fooths the fancy, grows weary of admira-
" tion, and defers the reft."

That *new raptures want fomething to footh
the fancy*, &c. will hardly bear. So long as
great

great and frefh delights laft, lefs are hardly
required, an anticlimax of enjoyment. But,
moreover, what is a ftronger proof of the
merit of a piece than its fupplying repeated
raptures? " O, 'tis too much for man, but
" let it ne'er be lefs!" Whatever may be
alleged for a truce of relief, few but envi-
ous perfons are difpleafed with being too
much delighted. Befides that, unity or uniformity is the perfection of a piece; when
the mind has prepared itfelf to be foothed,
wit may indeed be not acceptable; but when
it is fet for wit, wit is expected. *Eafily* is
in this quotation unmeaning, as *enough* and
fufficiently fometimes in thefe *Lives*, ufed as
the adjuncts of indifference or ill, is at beft
an unmeaning, and rather indeed an abfurd
idiom, or low humour.

" Who can forbear to think of an en-
" chanted caftle, with a wide moat and
" lofty battlements, walls of marble and
" gates of brafs, which vanifhes at once
" into air, when the deftined knight blows
" his horn before it?"

Somewhat

Somewhat like this, was the fudden change in the nation in favour of prerogative, after the diffolution of the parliament at Oxford ; and indeed fomething not unlike it has happened in thefe times.

" Perfonal refentment, though no laudable motive to fatire, can add great force to general principles."

Much has been faid on both fides concerning perfonal fatire, which goes by the name of *lampoon*. It is certain that a perfon labouring under the injuries of power, has often no poffibility of redrefs: in which cafe, let lawyers fay what they will, reafon will put in its claim, and even religion will not filence common fenfe; and though a public robber may feel the force of general fatire, a private oppreffor muft expect individual retaliation ; a farcafm muft be to the fufferer inftead of an action, and a point of wit for a point of law. There is, however, little danger in libelling a poor man, who, were he able to make experiment of the law, would find it a whited fepulchre.

Of

Of the ſtrictures, one on Brady, and the
other on Trapp, the former contains a wit-
ticiſm of the direct kind, of which our author is ſparing ; the other, one of thoſe dry
ſarcaſms of which he was very fond. Both
of theſe may be juſt: but he betrays a
prejudice againſt blank verſe, which being profeſſedly the beſt vehicle of tragedy,
cannot be improper for epic ; and I have
obſerved, that after having been for ſome
time uſed to blank verſe, an unpropitious
denomination, the jingle of rhyme has ſeem-
ed to me childiſh.

" The works of Chaucer, upon which
" this kind of rejuvenſcence has been be-
" ſtowed, require little criticiſm."

Chaucer is no favourite with our author ;
but his wit was brilliant, and his humour
powerful; too hoſtile to the chicanery of
prieſtcraft for Johnſon, and very extraordinary at that time of day ; but ſometimes in-
decent.   Dryden is probably partial in ſet-
ting *Palamon* and *Arcite*, on a level with the
Eneid ; yet Chaucer was a great genius,
                                             and

and deemed the primo-genitor of Englifh
poetry. His *Flower and Leaf*, paft over by
the fmoak-loving Johnfon, is charmingly
modernized : the nineteen firft lines in particular are fo delightful, and contain fo incomparable a fketch of the beauty of
Spring, that they fhould charm all readers:

" Now turning from the wint'ry figns, the Sun
" His courfe exalted thro' the Ram had run ;
" And, whirling up the fkies, his chariot drove
" Thro' Taurus and the lightfome realms of love,
" Where Venus from her orb defcends in fhow'rs,
" To glad the ground, and paint the fields with flow'rs ;
" When firft the tender blades of grafs appear,
" And buds that yet the blaft of Eurus fear,
" Stand at the door of life and doubt to cloath the year ;
" Till gentle heat, and foft repeated rains
" Make the green blood to dance within their veins :
" Then, at their call, embolden'd out they come,
" And fwell the gems and burft the narrow room ;
" Broader and broader yet their blooms difplay,
" Salute the welcome fun and entertain the day :
" Then from their breathing fouls the fweets repair
" To fcent the fkies and purge the unwholfome air ;
" Joy fpreads the heart, and with a gen'ral fong
" Spring iffues out, and leads the jolly months along,"

" With the fimple and elemental paf-
" fions, as they fpring feparate in the mind,
" he

" he feems not much acquainted ; and fel-
" dom defcribes them but as they are com-
" plicated by the various relations of fo-
" ciety, and confufed in the tumults and
" agitations of life." I queftion if this is
not as juft a characteriftic of himfelf as of
Dryden, whom Congreve affirms to have
been likewife humane, though he was impatient of rivalry and favage ; for with
cruelty and favagenefs to other writers, was
Johnfon's tendernefs combined.

" *I knew*, (fays Dryden,) *that they were*
" *bad enough to pleafe, even when I wrote*
" *them*," is the true *concordia difcors* of wit.
But why fhould our author fuppofe that
Dryden fhould pleafe himfelf with the
fuftian which he thus ftigmatizes ? What
follows is not the dictate of nature, nor often
of religion, but of the world, from which
Johnfon was not emancipated, how much
foever he was from the flefh and the devil.

" He had more mufic than Waller, more
" vigour than Denham, and more nature
" than Cowley," is a broken appofition.

Mufic

Mufic was Waller's excellence; vigour Denham's; but nature was not Cowley's.

" The haftinefs of his productions might
" be the effect of neceflity; but his fubfe-
" quent neglect could hardly have any
" other caufe than impatience of ftudy."
Revifions of paft productions, muft doubtlefs interrupt the compofition of new ; alfo,
his readers had not to regret that their edi-
tions were fuperfeded by others, and the
vigorous racinefs of his genius did not ftag-
nate in dregs, though his wit fometimes ran
foul.   However, a remarkable inftance of
his diflike of trouble, is his difcovery in
writing the latter part of his preface to his
Juvenal, that he had not fpelt *fatire* right,
and that, as he fays, he thought it not
worth while to look it over again to correct it.   But I am inclined to think, that
the etymology is *fatyr*, from the fatyrs.

" As thefe lines" *(of fourteen fyllables)*
" had their break on *cæfura*, always at the
" eighth fyllable, it was thought, in time,
" commodious to divide them ; and qua-
                                        " trains

" trains of lines, alternately confifting of
" eight and fix fyllables, make the moft
" foft and pleafing of our lyric meafures ;
" as,

> " *Relentlefs Time, deftroying power,*
> " *Which ftone and brafs obey;*
> " *Who giv'ft to ev'ry flying hour*
> " *To work fome new decay.*"

And when there is only one rhyme in the
twenty-eight fyllables, there is no other difference but the ranging them in two lines,
or in four.

" In examining their propriety, it is to
" be confidered, that the effence of verfe
" is regularity; and its ornament, variety."
An excellent, if a new obfervation.

" The Englifh Alexandrine breaks its
" lawful bounds, and furprifes the reader
" with two fyllables more than he ex-
" pected."

Of this there is a fine inftance in Pope's
Temple of Fame ;—

" Around

" Around a thoufand winged wonders fly,
" Borne by the trumpet's blaft, and fcatter'd thro' the fky.

But there is in Dryden's Eneid an incomparable couplet, in which the Alexandrine is overtopped by a double one, or verfe of fourteen fyllables;—

" For thee the Ocean fmiles, and fmooths her wav'y breaft,
" And Heav'n itfelf with more ferene and purer light is
" bleft."

And if a common verfe of ten had preceded in the fame rhyme, it would have been a moft beautiful climax of numbers, as thus,—

For thee Aurora fpreads her fpangled veft,
For thee the Ocean fmiles, and fmooths her wav'y breaft,
And Heav'n itfelf with more ferene and purer light is bleft.

Regular exactnefs in poetry, Virgil, whofe verfification is admired by all, even affected to break. As to bracing of triplets, it deftroys the furprife of the reader, who, if he has a quick eye and ready modulation of his voice, will perceive and exprefs them readily enough without mechanical affift-

F   ance.

ance. Our author has written this great poet's life with candour, analized his character with much ingenuity, and difmiffed him with a genteel and juft eulogium.

SMITH.

SMITH.

" 'TWERE to be wifhed."—Indefinite
and ftrange, where the fenfe might
be grammatically and clearly afcertained!
Were, is continually ufed even by good authors, inftead of *would be*; and here, *'Twere*,
fhould be, *It is*. However, this charaćter
of Smith, by Oldfworth, though doubtlefs
ftrained, is, in my opinion, a mafterpieçe of
panegyric.

Why are we not told the reafon of Smith's
name being really *Neal?*

How do, " His play" *(Phædra)* " pleafed
" the critics, and the critics only;" and,
" the learned rejećt it as a fchool-boy's
" play;" and then again, " it is a fcholar's
" play;" all agree?

Neal, alias *Smith*, alias *Rag*, was altogether an odd charaćter. The nickname of
Rag, puts me in mind of the frequent in-

F 2   attention

attention to drefs in ftudious perfons. Thofe
of both fexes are by their ruling regard
naturally diverted from it. The female
fcholar is fonder of an elegant book than
of a handfome gown, or perhaps than even
of a handfome fellow : and a witty male
one of a fatire, than of a razor.

" I am difappointed by that ftroke of
" death which has eclipfed the gaiety of
" nations, and impoverifhed the public ftock
" of harmlefs pleafure!"

A horrid anticlimax! But that is not
the worft. Johnfon, after his effufions of
friendfhip to the manes of Garrick, could
not hold back a Parthian kick of *harmlefs
pleafure*, and a piece of affected contempt,
engendered perhaps by Garrick's comparifon of him with his own Profpero in the
Rambler, even in the contemplation of death.
Indeed he always treated him in fuch a manner as would tempt one to exclaim, *deliver
me from fuch a friend as Johnfon!* Perhaps,
mortified with the indifferent reception of
his *Irene*, he could not help transferring
the

the ill tafte of the people to difguft to
Garrick, notwithftanding his friend's efforts
in its favour. It will be always remembered that popular, as were Pope and
Johnfon, neither of them have furnifhed
the theatre with a lafting play, that Dryden could make in a breath.

The ingenious author of the life of Chatterton obferves, that " his imagination, like
" Dryden's, was more fertile than correct ;"
but, in the Doctor's opinion, Dryden's mind
was not lefs correct than Pope's, though a
victim to hafte.

DUKE'S

DUKE'S

LIFE is a precious morfel, in which there is however a piece of wittinefs;—" an " age when he, that would be thought a " wit, was afraid to fay his prayers,"

KING'S

L IFE ſhews his ſenſe, in preferring eaſe
and an apple-pye, to the jargon and
iniquity of law.

SPRAT

SPRAT

A FFORDS an inftance of a man being
furnifhed with a bifhoprick by means
of his acquaintance with Cowley, who, himfelf, was almoft ftarving.

LORD

LORD HALLIFAX'S

LIFE declares the difpofition of the bio-grapher to a Whig patron of literature, who is enumerated among the moft eminent poets, yet is defpifed. One good line he neverthelefs produced ;—

" He hung upon their rear, or lighten'd in their face.

PARNELL.

PARNELL.

" THE defcription of *barrennefs.*" I have often wondered at the fmallnefs of Irifh crops,—

    " And half an acre's corn is half a fheaf."

His verfes to Pope are very good.

GARTH.

GARTH

WAS a good poet, a good phyſician,
and an honeſt man; and more than
merely and paſſively ſo.

ROWE.

ROWE.

" THE character of *Lothario* feems to
" have been expanded by Richard-
" fon into *Lovelace* ; but he has excelled his
" original, in them oral effect of his fiction."

Califta's foliloquy is fine. *Clariffa* is, I
think, Richardfon's mafter-piece, unlefs
Clementina's fimplicity, fuch as Richardfon alone was capable of drawing, gives the
palm to the ftory of *Grandifon*, generally
deemed beyond human nature ; yet in accomplifhments, the *admirable Crichton* feems
to have much exceeded him ; but then little
is faid of Crichton's virtues and the excellence of his heart.

As to Rowe's want of worth, it is to be
hoped that he who knew how to feize the
hearts of others, did not want one himfelf.
As to his comedy of the *Biter*, though he
had no teeth, ftill he might be a match
for barking critics. Our author gives fo
high

high a character of his Lucan, that it feems inconfiftent with his encomium of Pope's Homer, if it does not give Rowe the palm of tranflation.

ADDISON.

ADDISON.

IT feems that Addifon was at four fchools;
Ambrofbury, Salifbury, Litchfield, and
the Chartreux; enough to fpoil the heads of
moft boys.

" But Addifon, who feems to have had
" other notions of a hundred pounds, grew
" impatient of delay, and reclaimed his
" loan by an execution."

I am forry our author has acquainted us
with this report of fuch a man, but wifh to
think it a miftake, or mifreprefentation.
But he takes a delight in depreciating Addifon's friendfhip to Steele, and indeed all
friendfhip; and enlarging on his rapaciouf-
nefs.

What inclines me to think this a miftake, is, that he mentions an execution as
the firft, inftead of laft, legal procefs; and,
moreover,

moreover, were it true, the motive might be good.

" Effay on the Georgicks, juvenile, fu-
" perficial, and uninftructive." Dryden was of a different opinion; and fo am I:—
A noble anticlimax.

" In this poem is a very confident and
" difcriminative character of Spenfer, whofe
" works he had never read." This feems odd. Addifon compliments Cowley in an admirable line of feven feet, or fourteen fyllables;—

" And plays in more unbounded verfe, and takes a nobler
" flight."

" While it was yet advanced no farther
" than the fimile of the angel."

It is ftriking to obferve, the noble imita-
tions to which two flights of the Pfalmift;
He came flying upon the wings of the wind,
XVIII. 10.—and! *He maketh the clouds his chariot, and walketh upon the wings of the wind,*
CIV.

CIV. 3. have given rife : viz. the laft couplet of this fimile of Addifon,—

    " And pleas'd the Almighty's orders to perform,
    " Rides in the whirlwind and directs the ftorm."

In Dryden's *Ceyx and Alcyone*, from Ovid,—

    " And now fublime fhe rides upon the wind."

Whence Pope borrowed,

    " Not God alone in the ftill calm we find,
    " He mounts the ftorm, and rides upon the wind."

Chatterton has,

    " And rides upon the pinions of the wind."

And the ftale rogue, Gray, has,

    " With arms fublime that float upon the air."

Addifon and Pope feem to have had the XVIII. more efpecially in view ; but Shakefpeafe, in *Romeo and Juliet*, the CIV.

    " Beftrides the lazy-paced clouds,
    " And fails upon the bofom of the air."

The defcription of this latter pfalm is fublimer

liner than the other ; but Sternhold has verfified the XVIII. much better, fo that Dryden is faid to have beftowed the higheft commendation on his verfion, in which he feems to have been particularly infpired to defcribe the Supreme Being :—

" On cherubs and on cherubims
   " Full royally he rode,
" And on the wings of mighty winds
   " Came flying all abroad."

The opera of *Rofamond* has not fo much reputation as it deferves. Sir John Hawkins obferves, that the villainy of Clayton's mufic preponderated againft the elegance and humour of the poetry.

The character given of it by Tickell is very juft, for it contains much fine thought in an enchanting variety of numbers, but is dafhed with Sir Trufty and Grideline.

" Addifon was frighted left he fhould be " thought a promoter of infurrection; and " the line was liquidated to *Britons, at-* " *tend !*"

G   And

And yet, had Addifon been a coward, he would have declined acceptance of the fecretaryfhip to the regency, when Lord Bolingbroke's papers and office were fealed up; a fituation at a time that will always mark his political confequence.

" That it" (the Drummer) " fhould have
" been ill received would raife wonder,
" did not we daily fee the capricious diftri-
" bution of theatrical praife,"—is a grain of Johnfon's own confolation for himfelf. But the *Drummer*, though born before *Irene*, a nine days wonder, that had juft time to cry, has furvived it.

" This cannot be faid of the few papers
" entitled the *Whig Examiner*."

Our author does full juftice to this paper, written by Addifon in anfwer to the *Examiner*, compofed by the Tories. Of the " fuperiority of his wit" to that of his comrades in the Spectator, his part comparable to Diana's figure among her
nymphs,

nymphs, or to a primary ftar in a conftella-
tion, is a proof.

" It" (*Marriage*) " neither found them
" nor made them equal." I cannot think
that Dr Johnfon would, on all occafions,
yield to blood fo great a fuperiority over
brains, as is there implied. I am forry fo
often to mention his worldly leaven which
yet he could cenfure in Dryden. And even
as to worldly circumftances; if his wife was a
Countefs,—Addifon was a Secretary of State;
an office at the fhrine of which Lords can bow.

" Every reader furely muft regret, that
" thefe two illuftrious friends, after fo
" many years paft in confidence and endear-
" ment, in unity of intereft, conformity of
" opinion, and fellowfhip of ftudy, fhould
" finally part in acrimonious oppofition."

Rather every reader will regret the entire mifreprefentation of this affair;—not
Steele, but Benfon, wrote the *Plebeian*; and
more than that, Steele fpoke in favour of
the bill in fpeeches now extant. It feems,

that

that Johnſon and Hawkeſworth, of whom
no life is written, whilſt Lowths has fur-
niſhed only a ſkeleton of a pamphlet, were
indeed no more than external friends; and
we do not find a zealous panygeric of
Hawkeſworth after his death by Johnſon,
like Addiſon's by Steele. And why did not
Johnſon, who was a Tory, lament the acrimonious oppoſition of Oxford and Bolingbroke?

" He demanded to be the firſt name in
" modern wit; and, with Steele to echo
" him, uſed to depreciate Dryden, whom
" Pope and Congreve defended againſt
" him." *Spence.*

How true ſoever is this, Dryden, Pope,
and Swift had all a keener or a rougher
edge of wit, ſtrictly ſo called. Addiſon's
was generally triturated into elegance; and
as he inſinuates of great writers, his, like
theirs, was Attic wit; that is, diſcourſes
through which a ſoul of thought is diffuſed;
and his thoughts, as well as ſtile, were expanded into ſentiment, and were indeed
ſeldom

feldom forcible or powerful. They were
not plain drams, but made into punch ;—
calomel was his phyfic, and fublimate was
Dryden's. " Moft wits will befpatter a
" friend when it bubbles," fays Addifon ;
but the tendernefs of his nature expreffed
his feverity at all times, and he wore wit
in a fcabbard.

" Of very extenfive learning he has given
" no proofs."

I do not pretend to judge of his learning.
But in the *Spectator* only, he has exhibited
conviction of his ftudies being far from confined to the claffics, ftronger than has his
biographer in the *Rambler*. What degrees
of his own learning his Dictionary may be
fuppofed to indicate, I cannot fay. In the
Spectator, a fingle paper of Addifon's is feen
to contain a hiftory of a fcience in miniature.
With what dexterity has he diffected the
Beau's head, and Coquette's heart ; and
Fielding fpeaks of him as eminently learned.

" He had read, with critical eyes, the
" important

" important volume of human life, and
" knew the heart of man from the depths
" of ftratagem to the furface of affectation."

Then furely he was qualified for politics,
if not for an official politician ; and, from
what is juft after quoted from Steele, wanted
nothing but courage to be a fluent fpeaker,
I agree with our author in the expreffion,
the important volume of human life, though
Addifon had not feen thefe *lives*. Important it is, but very difagreeable ; a volume
that repels perfons of high intellect from
its contemplation, to feek folace and entertainment in fcenes of romance ; that, after
the reading of a page of that of which all
pages are alike ; and more than ever now,
that the intercourfe of the world has been
facilitated, and pride and felfifhnefs deftitute of a virtue, and polifhed barbarity have
become univerfal, bidding wife men withdraw themfelves to imaginary regions of
peace and benevolence.

Of human life, vice is the current coin;
and, as Dr. Kelley obferves, " he who erects
" a fure

" a fure edifice, muft ground it on the
" foolifhnefs of mankind." A certain foundation indeed, however the fantaftic fuper-
ftructures may vary.

" Of the next couplet, the firft verfe, be-
" ing included in the fecond, is therefore
" ufelefs."

If the latter of thefe lines,

" 'Tis this that fhakes our country with alarms,
" And gives up Rome a prey to Roman arms,"

is conftrued into tautology, it is almoft impoffible to write a poem without it; ampli-
fication and even repetition being beauties
in poetry. The new miniftry could not
have defired a better conclufion, it tending
to put a ftop to the jars of party, and reconcile the nation to the peace.

" Who that ever afked fuccour from Bac-
" chus, was able to prevent himfelf from
" being enflaved by his auxiliary."

What is meant by *his auxiliary*, I know
G 4   not.

not. It is reported of the two friends, that
Steele, who certainly had pleafantry, would
entertain the company till he grew mellow;
and that then Addifon would take up the
converfation. Generous liquors are of fer-
vice to conftitutions whofe fluids want ac-
celeration.

" His delight was more to excite merri-
" ment than deteftation; and he detects
" follies rather than crimes ;" in which he
alfo complied with his genius, more Ho-
ration than Juvenalian.

" He has faid, not very judicioufly, in
" his character of Waller,"

 " Thy verfe could fhew e'en Cromwell's innocence,
 " And compliment the ftorm that bore him hence.
 " Oh! had thy Mufe not come an age too foon ;
 " But feen great Naffau on the Britifh throne,
 " How had his triumph glitter'd in thy page. '

" What is this but to fay, that he who
" could compliment Cromwell, had been
" the proper poet for King William."

Not to cavil at *had been*, for *would have*
been,

been, it feems that our author, when he wrote
this, entertained a tendernefs for the Protec-
tor, our liberties and religion, though William
and Mary, like Brutus, were conftrained to
facrifice filial duty to patriotifm. Indeed tender minds are unfit and incapacited for public
affairs in general, even for the office of a juftice
of peace. Be that as it may, the fentiment
of Addifon, in thefe lines, was but this: *If
thy verfe could fhew fuch an ufurper as Cromwell in a favourable light, in what bright colours
wouldeft thou have painted King William!* The
firft couplet ought not to be taken literally;
it meaning no more than that Waller threw
a glory on Cromwell, not that Addifon intended a comparifon between him and William; and all this Johnfon very well knew.

" That longs to *launch* into a nobler ftrain."

Be the metaphor good or bad, the fabri-
cator foon after *galloped, fung,* or *launched*
himfelf into a place of three hundred a-
year.

" It is not eafy to paint in fong, or to
" fing in colours."

Our author here ftrikes at the root of
metaphor with a blunder ftolen from Addifon himfelf, in his remarks on a letter of
Lord Bolingbroke. Poetry and Painting
are fifter arts: the bufinefs of both being
defcription, they may be reciprocally ufed
to figure and illuftrate each other. Our
author himfelf has thefe words, Vol. I.
p. 235.—" To put thefe materials to *poeti-*
" *cal ufe*, is required an imagination capa-
" ble of *painting nature*, and realizing fic-
" tion." Every one can produce a hundred inftances of metaphor more open to
ridicule than this. Two pages ago, he
talked of a *broken metaphor*. *What*, fays a
fmart, *is a metaphor a faggot, or a fiddle-
ftick?* By the way, *broken*, is a metaphori-
cal epithet affixed to *metaphor*.

An attention to fuch hyper-criticifms
would reduce all writings to lees. And it
feems (fee the fequel) extraordinary that an
angel, of the agency of which kind of beings we have little or no idea, fhould in
driving a ftorm, too much refemble a General's conducting a battle for a fimile.

" For

" For not only Cato is vanquifhed by
" Cæfar, but the treachery and perfidiouf-
" nefs of Syphax prevails over the honeft
" fimplicity of Juba ; and the fly fubtlety
" and diffimulation of Portius over the ge-
" nerous franknefs and openheartednefs of
" Marcus." *Dennis.*

But how does all this end ? In favour of
the meritorious perfons: and, the fate of
Cato excepted, or rather the triumph of
Cæfar, fuicide being holden heroic by the
Romans, the cataftrophe was in a manner
happy : on the whole, it is of a mixed nature. The foliloquy of Cato is an imitation
of Hamlet ; and perhaps Hamlet's was de-
rived from Job, chap. iii. v. 17, 18, &c.

" An inftructor, like Addifon, was now
" wanting (to precede the great Johnfon)
" whofe remarks being fuperficial, might
" be eafily underftood ; and being juft,
" might prepare the mind for more attain-
" ments"—(for the fefquipedalia of our author. Addifon had the art of fmoothing
learning, by avoiding technical and hard
terms,

terms, and captivating in a neat diſha-
bille.

I may obſerve, that in all nice explanations, words ſhould be uſed in their ſtrict,
proper ſenſe, when poſſible ; a figure of
ſpeech being the adoption of one ambiguity
to explain another. Though Johnſon deals
out the praiſe of his predeceſſor eſſayiſt with
a rather grudging hard, his character of
him is altogether juſt, and not uncandid ;
and more favourable to his unaffected poetry
than has been the general opinion thereof ;
and whatever ſuggeſtions he may have
thrown out elſewhere, the *Spectator* will always have more readers than the *Rambler*,
which, weighty as is its matter, perhaps
falls ſhort in animation and allurement, of
the *Adventurer*. I am inclined to think
that the Spectators have had more readers
than the writings of Pope, or any whatſo-
ever of their ſtanding.

HUGHES.

HUGHES.

" HE judged fkilfully enough of his own intereft."

From what follows, it appears that this is ironical—Hughes was a Whig.

I fhould like to know if the Doctor himfelf knew what he meant by Mr. Duncombe's " *blamelefs elegance*."

" The character of his genius I fhall " tranfcribe from the correfpondence of " Swift and Pope."

Knowing the juft ftigma inflicted by Horace, *mediocribus poetis*, this choice of fixing Hughes's character cannot but be confidered as injurious. It does not clearly appear what Swift meant by faying " he is too great a poet for me," which taken by itfelf might be deemed a compliment, and was the truth. Swift is no better than a dog-

grel

grel poet ; and Pope might have recollected
that himfelf could not write a play. The
charaĉter, it is true, of an *honeft man*, is certainly highly eftimable, and fuch an one as
Hughes found the value of when on his
death bed, when literary fuccefs was put in
the fcale with religious confidence. Our
author remarks, that his " reputation was
" fo far advanced, that the public began to
" pay reverence to his name." And he may
be juftly ranked with the fecond-rate genius's, fuch as Steele, Congreve, Prior, and
even Addifon ; and his contemners, Swift
and Pope. There is a beautiful groupe of
verfes at the end of the fourth aĉt of the
Siege of Damafcus, which were greatly re-
lifhed by Quin :

" Think that ye all to certain triumph move;
" Who falls in fight, yet meets the prize above ;
" There, in the gardens of eternal fpring,
" While birds of paradife around you fing,
" Each with his blooming beauty by his fide,
" Shall drink rich wines that in full rivers glide,
" Breathe fragrant gales o'er fields of fpice that blow,
" And gather fruits immortal as they grow :
" In blifs extatic, your whole powers employ,
" And ev'ry fenfe be loft in ev'ry joy."

I will

I will conclude the life of Hughes with noticing a very good obfervation of his on compofing :—that when a piece has lain by for a while, the author, whofe mind the thoughts have fomewhat, but not entirely relinquifhed, will be enabled to judge of them himfelf impartially, and to revife them with advantage, efpecially to reform obfcurities.

SHEFFIELD,

SHEFFIELD,

I N his anfwer both to King William and
the prieft, fhewed a blunt honefty; but
I do not underftand the latter about tran-
fubftantiation; literature, though not Milton, is indebted to him as a noble ftudent.

PRIOR.

PRIOR.

" HE was perhaps willing enough to
" leave his birth unfettled, in hope,
" like Don Quixotte, that the hiftorian of
" his actions might find him fome illuftri-
" ous alliance."

This does not well agree with his own
epithet, " Nobles and Heralds,"—which
breathes a fpirit of bravado againft ancef-
try: and, in my opinion, the creator is
more eftimable than the inheritor of grandeur ; nothing beyond exemption from idi-
otifm being neceffary for the latter.

" There was now a call for writers, who
" might convey intelligence of paft abufes,"
&c.

At the time thefe *lives* were written, there
feemed to be a call for writers to explore
the reafon why all the world almoft had
confpired againft a nation which had fpent

H   its

its blood and treasures in defence of the rights of mankind.

" Whatever Prior obtains above medio-
" crity, seems the effect of struggle and
" toil. He has many vigorous, but few
" happy lines ; he has every thing by pur-
" chase, and nothing by gift ; he had no
" *nightly visitations* of the muse ; no infusions
" of sentiment or felicities of fancy."

It requires such a judge as Dr. Johnson to make these discriminations ; who, on the whole, allows Prior wit, art, and laboured metre, but not genuis: but if he had not the gift of poetical sleep, he had a considerable share in procuring repose to Europe, though he is unwilling to grant him either sentiment or passion. Henry and Emma made me weep. And, he being both correct and easy, the former admitted by Johnson, the latter by others, elegance must be confessed to be the result.

" In his preface to *Solomon*, he proposes
" some improvements, by extending the
" sense

" fenfe from one couplet to another, with
" variety of paufes. This he has at-
" tempted, but without fuccefs; his inter-
" rupted lines are unpleafing, and his fenfe,
" as lefs diftinct, is lefs ftriking." A motley
combination of rhyme with blank verfe.

CONGREVE.

" LANGUOR of convalefcence," truly Johnfonian. Congreve's noted declaration to Voltaire, has received the reprehenfion it deferves. However, Addifon attributes his ceafing to write, as a mark of his prudence in knowing when to leave off. Indeed a mere gentleman, one of a fmooth bag of pebbles proud of his *vis inertia,* is as infignificant a being as can be conceived.

" His comedies have therefore, in fome
" degree, the operation of tragedies; they
" furprize rather than divert, and raife ad-
" miration oftener than merriment." That is, they are witty, but not humourous; but they hardly much refemble tragedies, unlefs in their baneful effect.

" Looking tranquillity." *Mourning Bride.*

Tranquillity is but a feeble word, and yet folemnity would not perhaps be a better.
——" By

—————————" By fate of war to prove
" The victor worthy of the *fair one's* love."

To be sure the application of the ladies'
epithet *fair*, to a heifer, unless an Europa,
is hardly worthy of a polite gallant. Be
that as it may, our author could not on a
less favourable occasion than this, omit an
opportunity of being merry on pastoral :
indeed fable is ill adapted to the pathetic,
and some of the lines quoted from Congreve
are rough and uncouth, and the words of
several of them interfected by the accent, as

" The hov'ring winds on down-y wings shall wait around,
" And catch, and waft to for-eign lands the flying sound
" Encompass'd all the ming-led mass of seas and lands."

A mode not allowable but in Pindarics, if
in them.

If our lexicographer had written, " He
" sometimes retains what *would have been*
" more properly omitted," instead of the
jargon, " he sometimes retains what *were*
" more properly omitted," it might have
been as well or better.

H 3   BLACKMORE.

BLACKMORE.

——" AND let it be remembered for his honour, that to have been
" once a fchool-mafter, is the only reproach
" which all the perfpicacity of malice, ani-
" mated by wit, has ever fixed upon his
" private life."

This is a fpecimen of fine irony, fevere as the animadverfion may feem. The pride and folly of mankind, and of nominal Chriftians is fuch, that it is their fupreme glory to mock and fpurn the humility of him whofe difciples they profefs themfelves, but with real contempt and hatred of him.

" To this cenfure, may be oppofed the " approbation of Locke," who hated po- etry as much as do the inhabitants of Cheapfide.

" The reft of the *Lay Monks* feem to be " (rather to have been) but feeble mortals,

" in

" in comparifon with the gigantic Johnfon,
" who yet, with all his abilities, and the
" help of the fraternity, could drive the
" publication but to forty papers, which
" were afterwards collected into a volume,
" and called in the title *A Sequel to the*
" *Spectator.*"

Thefe biographies form together the literary hiftory of a century, which might
be termed the golden one.

" His account of *Wit*, will fhew with how
" little clearnefs he is content to think, and
" how little his thoughts are recommended
" by his language."

This cenfure, though fevere, is juft. As
he at one time wrote in the ftile of the
merchant and trader, fo in this defcription
of genius, rather than of *wit*, he difcovers
the phyfician. Poor Blackmore, like Dennis, had the luck to be a whetftone as well
as a wit.

" One paffage, which I have found al-

" ready twice, I will here exhibit, becaufe
" I think it better expreffed than could be
" expected from the common tenour of his
" profe."

As to the quotation alluded to: it is certain that many put confidence in an accidental profeffion of religion, without a fenfe
of it, as they poffefs a thoughtlefs kind of
love of their country ; the former calculated
to the Romifh religion, and the latter to
French government.

FENTON.

FENTON.

" *MARIAMNE* is written in lines of
ten fyllables, with few of thofe re-
" redundant terminations which the drama
" not only admits but requires, as more
" nearly approaching to real dialogue."

This correfponds with my idea. With
thefe lines, confifting of eleven fyllables,
Shakefpeare abounds more than Milton; of
which the following in Cato are examples:

" The wide, th' unbounded profpect lies before me;
" But fhadows, clouds, and darknefs reft upon it."

" Steele, in fome parts of the *Guardian*,
" had praifed Ambrofe Philips." This
feems to be a fmall miftake; all the papers
on paftoral poetry, except one by Pope in
his own praife, being by Tickell.

GAY.

GAY.

" HIS *What d'ye call it*, a kind of mock " tragedy, in which the images " were comic, and the action grave." From difproportions always proceed burlefque, not feldom nearly the confequence of common things invefted with pompous diction in the Rambler.

" His friends perfuaded him to fell his " fhare."—With all due fubmiffion to the lexicographer, I apprehend that *endeavoured to perfuade*, would have been more proper; *perfuaded to*, being nearly tantamount to *prevailed with*.

" For this he is faid to have been pro- " mifed a reward, which he had doubtlefs " magnified with all the wild expectations " of indigence and vanity."

Why would Johnfon always delight to degrade

degrade genius, and render it the contempt
of rich fools?

" His *fables* feem to have been a favourite
" work ; for, having publifhed one volume,
" he left another behind him."

Experience has proved them to be excellent, and the introduction to them is admirable. From the latter part of them, it
feems ftrange that the neglect of a court
fhould have rendered him miferable, whofe
character entitled him to look down on
courtiers as the buzzing infects of a day.
Query, Was the humourous paper in the
Adventurer, concerning an author's reading
his tragedy to a great perfon, aimed at
Gay? The form of his fables is, I think,
original, and, like the *Beggar's Opera*, they
will hardly be equalled.

He was not a great, but a witty, adroit,
various, and original writer. It is obferv-
able that Pope has remarked his fimplicity, and Johnfon his vanity. Our author,
intent upon rhodomantade, alfo denomi-
nates

nates him a writer adapted to barbarians, becaufe of his plaintive paftoral of *Dione*: but perhaps he who prefers the world as it is man's, to it as it is God's, is rather a barbarian.

LANSDOWN,

LANSDOWNE,

IT may be perceived from our author's mean opinion of him, was a lover as well as lord : as to his poetry, I have a better opinion of it than our author, whofe mind was, in fome refpects, as narrow as a crane's neck.

YALDEN.

YALDEN.

" WHEN Namur was taken by King
" William, Yalden made an ode.
" There was never any reign more cele-
" brated by the poets than that of Wil-
" liam, who had very little regard for fong
" himfelf, but happened to employ minif-
" ters who pleafed themfelves with the
" praife of patronage."

This is a moft pungent fting of contempt; but it is certainly fhameful to attribute good actions to worthlefs motives, and
as foolifh for Johnfon to declare himfelf a
Jacobite in every page. As to his laughing
at poetry, he had indeed no relifh for any
but didactic; and had he been apprehen-
five that ever a golden age (let no punfter
remind us of his penfion) would be on earth,
how fervently would he have prayed to be
delivered from it; and how infipid and
wretched muft he have deemed the condition of Adam and Eve before their fall,
when

when neither taverns, venifon, nor flander,
were in being!

The laft *and* in the laft paragraph of
Yalden's life is fuperfluous.

TICKELL.

TICKELL.

" TO Tickell, however, cannot be re-
" fufed a high place among the
" minor poets."

If by the term *minor poet*, the quantity
of his poetry is meant, he is properly fo
called ; but if the quality is thereby underftood, it is a difparagement.

HAMMOND'S

L OVE-complaints were precious food
for the maw of Johnſon, who in mumbling them did not, however, perceive that
the alternate quatrain has a ſolemnity ſuited
to elegy.

SOMER-

SOMERVILLE

WAS not likely to be followed far by him over fix-bar gates; but has ftarted a Savage in his hunt.

SAVAGE.

SAVAGE.

" T O be humane, generous, and can-
" did, is a very high degree of me-
" rit in any cafe ; but thofe qualities de-
" ferve ftill greater praife, when they are
" found in that condition which makes al-
" moft every other man, for whatever rea-
" fon, contemptuous, infolent, petulant,
" felfifh, and brutal."

If this fevere animadverfion, too characteriftic of all mankind, is peculiarly applicable to players, fome fhew of reafon may
perhaps be affigned, poffibly, that continually converfant with fictitious mifery and
calamity, they may lofe conception of the
reality ; and thus tragedians may refemble
butchers; and Savage might be well afhamed
of being enrolled with them, curfed as he
was moreover with the twin curfes of humanity, pride, and poverty, in their full
extent. From what caufe foever proceeds,
if the cenfure is juft, this calloufnefs : To

the

the generous humanity, fufficient to cover
a multitude of fins, of two players, Mr.
Wilkes and Mrs. Oldfield, let me add the
name of Mr. Samuel Foote ; whofe noble
conduct towards the arch impoftor, Charles
Price, ftamps him, always acknowledged
admirable for his wit and ingenuity, and
highly eftimable, as he is now known to
have been for his learning, and amiable for
his unfufpicious finccrity, the certain crite-
rion of a good mind, unacquainted with de-
ceit, with the character of exalted Chriftianity. In the life of Price (written with a
not unpleafant dry archnefs) it appears that
Mr. Foote could forgive, and even befriend
the man who villainoufly and brutally endeavoured to convert his confidence and
kindnefs to his entire deftruction.

" He always himfelf denied that he was
" drunk, as had been generally reported."

Then it muft have been a duel with Sin-
clair and the maid. Drunkennefs cannot indeed be generally admitted for an excufe
for any crime: yet, if malice prepenfe, as
cannot

cannot be denied, conftitutes the heinouf-
nefs of every one, real drunkennefs, in
which the blood is warm, is a great miti-
gation in *foro confcietiæ*, for none will con-
tend, *a priori*, that drunkennefs is a crime
equal to murder.

" Good is the confequence of evil," is a
pofition of dangerous tendency, in which
Johnfon verged towards Mandeville. If indeed, by the prefent depravity of human
nature, it cannot be but *offences muft arife,
woe be to him by whom they come*, fince each
individual is a free agent. And the fuggef-
tion that vice may be expiated by its own
fufferings in this world, where it is triumphant is very dangerous.

" That he fold fo valuable a perform-
" ance"—The Wanderer.

Savage, accurate and negligent, fenfible
and foolifh, was in an extraordinary manner at once carelefs about the prefent and
the future, with a quick fenfe of both ; it
being difficult to determine which he va-

I 3   lued

lued moſt a good dinner or fame: ſo ſays
Horace, *Carpe diem* ; and *Exegi monumentum.*

He was kind to his perjured accuſer, and
ungrateful to a generous patron. He was
preciſe and extravagant; tragical and capricious; employed on jollity and comma's;
freaks and ſemicolons. Wit and prudence
are not often united; far indeed from being united in him, yet with wit he
combined minuteneſs. What a happy
thoughtleſsneſs did he poſſeſs; who could
at eaſe entertain himſelf and his companions with pleaſantry and gibes, when an
empty pocket would have been continually
in the thoughts of another.

  " So comes the reck'ning when the banquet's o'er:
  " The dreadful reck'ning, and men ſmile no more."

was not anticipated by him.

  " He (Tyrconnell) was ſo much provoked
  " by the wit and virulence of Savage, that
  " he came with a number of attendants,
  " that did no honour to his courage, to
  " beat him at a coffee-houſe."

It

It appears ftrange, that in fuch a country as this, fuch outrages fhould be heard of ; and that the fufferer had better fit down quiet, than feek legal redrefs. This, however, was the cafe before the miraculous paffing of Lord Mansfield's Privilege Bill ; which, excellent as it is whilft it lafts, wants an amendment to render it completely efficacious ; that where the jury give damages to a certain amount to be fpecified, the plaintiff fhould have, not nominal, but real cofts of fuit, with the option, however, for the defendant to have them taxed. This would at once be a check on the fhameful impofitions of attornies, and transfer the additional expence of afcertaining the cofts, from the injured to the injurer.

" The fpirit of Mr. Savage, indeed, ne-
" ver fuffered him to folicit a reconcilia-
" tion."

It is indeed difficult, efpecially for a gentleman, to live long with any degree of fatisfaction in a ftate of dependance on a fellow-fubject ; an argument for monarchy

I 4   under

under which the meaneſt exciſeman or ſol-
dier conſiders himſelf as the ſervant of none
but a crowned head. Mankind are too
wayward for each other to preſerve a due
medium : the ſuperior will act the rigid
churchman ; and the inferior the ſtubborn
puritan, and fancy affronts : ſays the poet,

" Were I to curſe the miſcreant I hate,
" Attendance and dependance be his fate !

Mr. Savage thought it neceſſary, to his
own vindication, to proſecute him in the
King's-Bench ! A redreſs wanting to complete his ruin.

" On a bulk, in a cellar, or in a glaſs-
" houſe among thieves and beggars, was to
" be found the author of the Wanderer."
Would a curious enquirer determine that
there are pleaſures peculiar to every ſitua-
tion. Savage's life exhibits an example of
ſurprizing irreſolution and folly ; yet nŏt
more ſurprizing than the improvidence of
mankind in general, in regard to futurity,
were not indeed the preſſure on the material ſcenes almoſt irreſiſtible in wordly
want :

want : but what can excufe others? A nig-
gard, being told how vain was his faving-
nefs, for that the fruits of it would be
quickly fquandered by his heir, made anfwer—that if his heir fhould have as much
enjoyment in fpending as he had in faving,
it would be great. And doubtlefs the œco-
nomift; the mafter of his money, his morals, and himfelf; poffeffes a tranquillity, a
bafis of happinefs unknown to him who
floats awhile on the ftream of diffipation,
perhaps to fink, the derifion and fcorn of
thofe who battened in his luxury and ruin,
feverer than poverty and hunger itfelf.
Foolifh as was Savage, his wafting his money at a tavern, was lefs fo than giving it
away to fharpers.

" He attempted in Wales to promote a
" fubfcription for his works, and had once
" hopes of fuccefs ; but in a fhort time af-
" terwards formed a refolution of leaving
" that part of the country."

He was volatile as mercury, and combuf-
tible as gunpowder ; never to be at reft,

and every minute liable to be blown up;
himfelf a wandering comet, who took not
delight in his aphelion.

" It is not without fome fatisfaction, that
" I can produce the fuffrage of Savage in
" favour of mankind.

It is hard to conceive what fhould induce
any one with eyes in his head, to think
well of mankind in general.

This life is written in a very eafy and entertaining manner ; it having been publifhed
many years ago, at which time Johnfon was
lefs quaint, atrabilious, conceited, and wayward than in his later years, and planned
it lefs haftily than the lives of the poets.
If he fometimes borders on tautology, it
fhould be confidered that in nice difcrimi-
nations it is very difficult to avoid obfervations nearly tautologous, without circum-
locutions and explanations which the reader
muft fupply. However, this *apology for the
life of Savage*, is by fome confidered as a
blot in Johnfon's character ; and indeed
morals

morals are herein ftretched to latitudinari-
anifm, fuch as, it may be feared, granted
himfelf a difpenfation ; for Johnfon expected
nothing of perfection either in writing or
morality, and fomething was due to fellow-
feeling with Savage. In this entertaining
hiftory, he rather talks than writes to the
reader ; directs him on the road to knowledge as if prefent ; informs him of the
characters and circumftances of the inhabitants as he paffes along, and becomes his
friend as well as companion, refembling the
manner of Plutarch's colloquial-like ftyle.

That part of my readers who are acquainted with Gregory's Life of Chatterton, can fcarcely be able to perufe the life
of Savage, without being difpofed to draw
fome comparifon between them. The author of Love and Madnefs, has indeed compared Chatterton with Mahomet. There is,
I confefs, this refemblance,—that they are
both

both confidered by many as impoftors : but though Chatterton talked of becoming a methodift, moft perfons will be inclined rather to compare the cant of Mahomet and Cromwell.

It appears that Chatterton's too true profeffion, and even boaft, that he was no Chriftian, was the fource of the moft poignant mifery in this world, and the caufe of his fad exit; the effect of pride, a folly which, however furprifingly it takes its abode in men of capacity, cannot poffibly refide in a breaft occupied with the wifdom of the gofpel—that fovereign and only antidote againft the cup of adverfity. It might be expected that genius fhould ftem the torrent of empty and fenfelefs vanity ; but this it is often found incapable of doing, unlefs fortified and cemented with religious philofophy ; of which the commixture of fenfe with weaknefs, and of fine parts with vulgarity in Chatterton, devoid of a dreg of economy, was a melancholy proof ; for his firft ftarving, and afterwards poifoning himfelf, can hardly be denominated

nated " the ftrong confcioufnefs of intellec-
" tual excellence," an expreſſion of the biographer in alleviation of the pride attributed to him.

Mr. Gregory, on the fuppofition that
Chatterton was the author or conftructor
of the poems under the name of Rowley,
of which few perfons entertain a doubt,
places his genius above Dryden's, and below only Shakefpeare's; thus allowing room
for him between Shakefpeare and Milton;
and totally ejecting the latter from competition with the former.

The probable truth is, that Chatterton
altered and fupplied chafms at leaft, if he
did not interpolate, fome ancient MSS. a-
mong which he might find the name of
Rowley, without which he would have
hardly undertaken fuch a work. This is a
falvo both for his veracity and genius,
otherwife at variance; and alfo reconciles
other circumftances. It is fuperfluous to
obferve, that in all things, and in myfteries
among the reft, the truth ufually lies in a
medium.

medium. Moreover, in the accomplifhment of his work, he might have unknown af-fiftance, as Mahomet is faid to have in the formation of the Alcoran : but the rapidity of the genius of Chatterton appears in one of his fprightly letters, in which he related that he fuddenly compofed feveral fongs the fame evening after the play.

It feems remarkable that Chatterton's ab-ftinence from animal food and fpirituous liquors, is alledged by this biographer as a proof of the preponderation of his vir-tues over his faults, though his profligacy towards women were acknowledged ; efpe-cially if it be confidered that ebriety is the beft, furely only excufe for diffolutenefs of that nature, as foolifh as wicked.

Refpecting the unhappy difappearance of this phenomonon, fome argue that fui-cide is as bad, and worfe, than murder, be-caufe precluding repentance ; but it feems but an indifferent apology for murder, to commit it to repent of it. It appears a felf-evident truth of analogy, till refined away,

away, that perfons have a better right to
difpofe of their own lives than of thofe of
others, as they have of their own property. As to the cowardice of fuicide, when
Shakefpeare makes Hamlet fay, that " con-
" fcience makes cowards of us all," did he
mean that it is cowardice in the miferable
to forbear fuicide? It is, however, unlucky
that the fineft foliloquy in the world, fhould
fuggeft a falfe and dangerous application.

A man poffeffed of neglected genius may
have fome excufe for a defperate refentment
againft mankind, but not of complaint
againft his maker, who previoufly endued
him with the moft valuable property in
his gift, if made a good ufe of ; and which,
had Chatterton exercifed a fmall degree of
prudence, would have furnifhed him whofe
firft literary profpects were much better
than Johnfon's, with a competence, and at
length, probably, with importance and
fame, *the defire of which is the lafting difeafe
of noble minds.*

It is but juftice to Mr. Gregory to add,
that

that this piece of Britifh biography is very inftructive and entertaining, interfperfed with excellent, found, and new reflections, and difcriminative fpecimens of an exact tafte in poetry and criticifm.

SWIFT.

SWIFT.

" THE advice and patronage of Sir William Temple." Swift feems to have imbibed his unreafonable predilection for the ancients from Sir William; for in the *Battle of the Books*, he has omitted fome of the moft eminent of all Britifh authors, alone fufficient to ftagger the ancients, even in literature as diftinguifhed from fcience.

Harley was a confounded queer dog.

" *Gulliver's Travels.*" As to the difficulty of criticifing this remarkable production, it may be termed an original peculiar romance, of more merit than is here allowed it, whilft we may hope that there is room in the univerfe, though not on earth, for beings as juft as the Houyhnms. Swift's knowledge of fea terms appears in it extraordinary, and I wifh that of mankind were exaggerated.

K   In

In regard to Stella, our author writes, not often the cafe, without conveying information.

" His *Tale of a Tub* has little refemblance
" to his other pieces. It exhibits a ve-
" hemence and rapidity of mind, a copi-
" oufnefs of images, and a vivacity of dic-
" tion, fuch as he afterwards never poffeff-
" ed, or never exerted. It is of a mode fo
" diftinct and peculiar, that it muft be con-
" fidered by itfelf ; what is true of that, is
" not true of any thing elfe which he has
" written."

This judgment is partly true and partly falfe. For, in my opinion, this Tale pof-feffes a cant-burlefque phrafe, not indeed to be found in any of Swift's writings, when he had formed a better ftile.

" The practice of faving being once ne-
" ceffary, became habitual ; and grew firft
" ridiculous, and at laft deteftable. But
" his avarice, though it might exclude plea-
" fure, was never fuffered to encroach upon
" his

" his virtue." How then could it be *de-teſtable?*

" Delany is willing to think, that Swift's
" mind was not much tainted with this
" groſs corruption before his long viſit to
" Pope." He who was paramount to Swift
in naſtineſs, would be poorly characteriſed
by a compariſon with a Hottentot, as Lord
Cheſterfield • denominated our author. In
many reſpects Johnſon and Swift had re-
ſemblance : both doctors ; both Jacobites ;
both men of ſtrong parts and authorita-
tive; and both deaf to muſic and ſentimental
poetry ; but I will not add that both min-
gled in a faction in order to initiate them-
ſelves to notice; though it is too well known,
that merit alone is of little avail, except
that in conjunction with virtue and ho-
neſty, it will not fail to render a writer
odious. Johnſon alſo follcwed Swift's pre-
cept and example, in adopting a ſtile conſiſting of *proper words in proper places,* ſeldom figurative.

POPE.

POPE.

" THIS, and this only, is told by Pope,
" who is more willing, as I have
" heard obferved, to fhew what his father
" was not, than what he was." He defined
his father, as Cowley did wit, and Congreve humour,—by negatives. It has fince
appeared that he was a linen-draper.

" *Ode on Solitude.*" A difcerning perfon,
might have perceived from this Ode, that
he was by nature a poet. Horace, and
other ancients, have obferved, that poets
delight in folitude. Cowley fays, that no
woods are by them thought thick enongh;
and *Melancholy marked Gray for her own.*
Pope's early works, the verfions of *Chaucer,*
and of the firft book of the *Thebais,* were alfo
fine fpecimens. As to the heroic poem of
" *Alcander,*" I do not thank Atterbury for
perfuading him to burn it; which doubtlefs contained fome bloffoms of genius; and
it is to be regretted, that dirt and jewels
were

were thrown away together, though it is probable that Pope might interſperſe them among his other works.

Wycherley ſeems to have infeſted Pope with Cowley's conſtant ſtretch after wit ; who was a full match for the antiquated ſcribbler at his own weapons ; never was flattery thicker ſown.

" He" (Cromwell) " was fond, and per-
" haps vain, of amuſing himſelf with poetry
" and criticiſm ; and ſometimes ſent his
" performances to Pope, who did not for-
" bear ſuch remarks as were now and then
" unwelcome."

How few there are that can bear the ſin-cerity of friendſhip, eſpecially if a little in-diſcreet! Indeed a ſpice of flattery, as of ſcandal, is almoſt neceſſary ; and often ſpurs a man on to worthy attempts. Atterbury and Cromwell were too ſincere, or poſſibly envioully ſincere to Pope : the former blam-ed rhyme and his Sakeſpeare, his all ; and Cromwell taxed him with ſtealing his roundeau.

roundeau. Walſh was wiſer; and without flattering him injurioully, retained his regard and gratitude as long as he lived, with the credit of initiating ſo great a poet;

> " Such late was Walſh, the Muſe's judge and friend,
> " Who knew full well to blame or to commend."

Any one can bolt his thoughts at random: ſomething is due to addreſs, to the way of the world, and to human nature. If one bluntly tells his friend all he knows to his diſparagement, his friend will be apt to ſuppoſe, in addition to this mortification, that part is ſtill ſuppreſſed. What is good-breeding but deference; and deference but negative flattery? Lowering ourſelves has the ſame effect as raiſing our companions; but common good-manners are too great a ſacrifice for the ſelf-importance of perſons of theſe poliſhed ages to make to ſociety; but the mortification of the humble and meek, is a neceſſary ingredient in the practice of high breeding.

> " The ſame year was written the *Eſſay on*
> " *Criticiſm*; a work which diſplays ſuch ex-
>   " tent

" tent of comprehenfion, fuch nicety of
" diftinction, fuch acquaintance with man-
" kind, and fuch knowledge both of ancient
" and modern learning, as are not often
" attained by the matureft age, and longeft
" experience."

Thefe circumftances deferve inveftigation;
the generality of mankind are unqualified
for reading or found obfervation, but, like
brutes, foon arrive at their *ne plus ultra.*
Their heads are like ground froft-bound,
unfufceptible of fcientific impreffion. On
the contrary, thofe of ingenious men are like
cultivated lands, in which every plant takes
root. Such feem to have minds that, to
continue the allufion, refemble foils, that,
according to fome have feeds* interfperfed

---

* The fpontaneous growth of plants is, I think, generally rejected; but I wifh to be informed how plants, the
feeds of which are not liable to be wafted by the wind, rife
quickly on earth taken from the bottom of wells, &c. Some
have recourfe to new ftrata of earths accumulated at the
flood; a ftrange and unfatisfactory account, as plants fpring
from earths taken from different depths. Men muft confefs
that they know nothing.

by

by nature at different depths, and withal
endued with a fuperior faculty of intuition.
But I obferve that a principal mean by
which fenfible and virtuous perfons by degrees arrive at the knowledge of mankind,
is inftinct, affifted by correfpondencies in the
minds of others; from the latter of which
it comes to pafs, that ill men become acquainted with the world fooner than good
men. Locke well fays, that the difference
between the ratiocination of human kind
and animals, confifts in the ability of the
former to combine, compare, and difcrimi-
nate ideas wherein the vulgar fail; and are
near akin to brutes and governed by cuftom; and on the proportions to a greater
or lefs endowment with fuch power, knowledge much depends*.

With whatever contempt Dennis was
treated, he was a *ftumbling block and rock of
offence*, as appears from Pope's and our au-

---

* For a very ingenious inveftigation concerning the ac-
quifition of the knowledge of mankind, fee an account of
Whitaker's obfervations on Mary Queen of Scots, in the
Englifh Review for July 1787.

thor's

thor's frequent occasion to mention him.
In truth, he was a man of learning and of
acute criticism; with a large share of envy
and malignity. His taste exposed him continually to the vexation of not being pleased
with the writers of those times; but nobody
can deny, if humour arises from the *repre-*
sentation of images in odd circumstances and un-
common lights, that, with all his dullness, he
had some share of it.

    " What is this wit?——
    " Where wanted, scorned; and envied where acquir'd."

There are two duplicities in the line,
which may be both made sense or non-
sense, as they are taken by the right or
wrong handle. It is plainly meant that those
who had not wit, scorned it (or rather pretended to scorn it) in others; and that
those who had it, were envied for it. But by
taking it the wrong way, it might be made
to mean, that those scorned the self-posses-
sion of it, who had it not; and that they envied it in themselves, who had it. So that
the latter part is equally exceptionable with
               the

the former, were either fo. As to the reft;
after Pope had defcribed Dennis as

" Staring tremendous with a threat'ning eye,
" Like fome fierce tyrant in old tapeftry."

Dennis was about even with him in calling
him " a downright monkey."

" From this account, given with evident
" intention to raife the lady's character, it
" does not appear that fhe had any claim
" to praife."

I am difpleafed to fee the author of the
Rambler a friend to monafteries, though
indeed religion may be better in a bad
fhape than in none at all. Hafty and culpable was the lady undoubtedly; but it
ought to be confidered, that no perfon ever
has been or can be happy againft violent
inclinations, with conftancy to a forced
partner for life.

It is generally allowed, that parents, and
perhaps guardians, fhould have a negative
voice; but this is not confirmed by the
marriage-

marriage-act, not even to parents when the
parties become of age. And what power
foever either the one or the other may naturally or legally poffefs, they ought to ex-
ert it no longer than to difcover whether
the parties are really engaged by a fettled
affection, which none can fever without fa-
crilege to nature, or only by fancy or caprice.
To thofe on whom love has made a deep
impreffion, nothing but its object can give
happinefs or peace of mind; confiderations
indeed that weigh little with the family-
pride of parents. Indeed the arguments
for and *againft* have been fo often adduced,
that it is impoffible to add to them, I will
therefore draw the matter to this point;
that an indulgence of paffion may be attended with happinefs, but that the difap-
pointment of it cannot.

" He feems to have done only that for
" which a guardian is appointed; he en-
" endeavoured to direct his niece till fhe
" fhould be able to direct herfelf." This
is, to be fure, fomething to the purpofe;
yet

yet amorous fury is too dangerous to be pent up. Can a foreign country cure it? *Can madneſs with reaſon agree? Can love be controuled by advice* to wait years, ages to them, of uncertainty? O Johnſon! thou didſt not learn this of Shakeſpeare.

This poem, and the epiſtle of *Eloiſe to Abelard*, are replete with poetical fire, and ſtrike the imagination with a captivating horror. A perſon endued with a true re-reliſh of poetry can never be tired of read-ing them—

   " Clouds interpoſe, waves roar, and winds ariſe."

Pope's pathetic poetry has certainly a charm hardly to be equalled; to which Tickell's elegy on Addiſon has, however, much re-ſemblance; and the lines quoted by our author from the *Mourning Bride*, are of the ſame claſs; and we may obſerve, that he has confeſſed the efficacy of religious verſe in theſe words;—" The mixture of religi-" ous hope and reſignation, gives an eleva-" tion and dignity to diſappointed love, which " images merely natural cannot beſtow."

As

As to the mighty eulogium on the *Rape of the Lock*, that " he had now exhibited " boundlefs fertility of invention," its machinery is but an ingenious expanfion of that in Shakefpeare's *Tempeft*.

" The fuperiority of Pope is fo ingeni-" oufly diffembled, and the feeble lines of " Philips fo fkilfully preferred, that Steele, " being deceived, was unwilling to print " the paper left Pope fhould be offended." It becomes not me to pronounce on this matter; but I believe that moft readers have been all along deceived. As to *feeble lines*, does any one expect others from rustics?

As to Pope's verfes to Jervais " betray-" ing his ignorance of painting," their generality might, one would have thought, have exempted them from that; and Dr. Warton's opinion is much different.

" He that runs againft time, has an an-" tagonift not fubject to caufualties."

This

This curious remark puts me in mind of a proverbial faying, which attended to, would have prevented a thoufand from ruin; and which, with the addition of *apparently*, renders it always practicable; and I ftrongly recommend to the reader, that he may not complain of the price of thefe remarks,—*never defer till to-morrow, what may be apparently as well done to-day*. This, with method in accounts, could not often fail to procure fortunes to men in bufinefs. Horace has fome verfes to this purpofe ;—

Sic mihi tarda fluurt ingrataque tempora quæ fpem, &c.

It is by perfeverance, not fnatches, that fteady Mr. Trot, who may be compared to time, gets money. A foot pace is preferable to a gallop, in which the rider is likely to be thrown ; which the Dutchman well knows. It is the hound, not the greyhound, that catches the hare at the long run; and both in compofing and reading, intervals are neceffary ; in the former, to look round and wait for ideas; and in the latter, to relieve the mind left fhe become jaded and moped, and pleafure ceafe ;
wherein

wherein bufinefs and letters differ. A perfon need not be always in his clofet to become a fcholar or an author, nor fhould
he; but he may always have a pencil about
him, that he may not forget his fugitive
ideas, or be revolving them in his mind to
his own anxiety and difguft of company.
As farthings and pence accumulate to
pounds, words accumulate to pages, and
thoughts to volumes: but the progrefs of
the fancy, the infinite-like operations of
the mind, are not like to material mecha-
nifm, keeping a regular pace.

Mr. Craggs's offer of providing for Pope,
was noble.

" That wrath which *hurl'd* to Pluto's gloomy reign."—

hurling fouls is a remarkable expreffion.

" Apollo's awful enfigns *grace* his hands."—

It feems that *grac'd*, was firft written. The
arbitrary promifcuous ufe of the prefent
and preterite tenfes, is very frequent and
convenient at leaft. Lord Kaims has a
good obfervation, that, in a paragraph, the
ufe

ufe firft of the prefent, and afterwards of the paft, is a kind of anticlimax.

The eight lines beginning with " But " Pallas"—are pointed wrong throughout, but are very fine.

" High on his helm celeftial lightnings play,"

is extremely poetical ; alfo,

" Crown her hero with diftinguifh'd praife,"

though plain language, has, like many parts of fcripture, a natural intrinfic fublimity,

I think that in

" A flood of glory burfts from all the fkies."

Burfts, how poetical foever, hardly well agrees with the admirable ftill fcene.

" It is not likely that Hallifax had any " benevolence to Pope; it is evident that " Pope looked on Hallifax with fcorn and " hatred."

Why fhould Pope look with fcorn and hatred on a nobleman who had raifed himfelf

felf to eminence, and then became the patron of letters? for he wrote to a third
perfon that he had his Lordfhip's patronage.

" In all this there was no hypocrify;
" for he confeffed that he found in Ad-
" difon fomething more than in any man;"
in the awkwardeft man breathing, according
to Chefterfield.

I wonder not that our author fhould be
fo fevere on Pope's grotto; efpecially as in
the higheft reach of art, he had converted
an inconvenience to an advantage. He relates his wifh for a ftatue, in fome verfes
fuch as thofe for which he teftified his
fondnefs. The following tranflation, which
he mentions, has fomething inimitably
foothing and delightful, and is, I think,
fuperior to the Latin; and I fear not to
rifk my opinion, that our language is fuf-
ceptible of more tendernefs and pathos
than either the Latin or Greek, which have
nothing to come up to our *ab's!* and *ob's!*
I allude to

L   " Nymph

" Nymph of the grot, thefe facred fprings I keep,
" And to the murmurs of the water's fleep ;
" Ah, fpare my flumbers, foftly tread the cave,
" And drink in filence, or in filence lave!"

I know not whether others, like me, fet their affections on pieces of writing fo as fometimes to difrelifh alterations even for the better, and can thus lay an equal claim to conftancy. It is hence perhaps that I prefer

" Whoe'er thou art, ah! gently tread the cave,
" Ah! bathe in filence, or in filence lave."

I have feen it, though *bathe* and *lave* are too like; I think it would be better,

Ah! fpare my flumbers, foftly tread the cave;
Ah! drink in filence, or in filence lave.

Repetitions have fometimes a fweet charm.

" He grew dexterous by practice, and
" every fheet enabled him to write the
" next with more facility. The books of
" Fenton have very few alterations by the
" hand of Pope."

It requires perhaps a better judge than
I am,

I am, to determine which preponderates, Addifon's pre-eminence in profe, or Pope's in verfe. But it feems extraordinary that Fenton's and Broome's verfification fhould equal their mafter's; and I do not perceive that Parnell's *Frogs and Mice* is unequal. I have heard Addifon's critique on Milton named as the beft that ever was, except Spence's on the *Odyffey*.

" I have heard of an ideot, who ufed to " revenge his vexations by lying all night " upon the bridge!" What means this? That Pope was an ideot?

" I know not whether there does not " appear fomething more ftudied and arti- " ficial in his productions than the reft, " except one long letter by Bolingbroke, " compofed with all the fkill and induftry " of a profeffed author."

Pope fpeaks of himfelf as throwing out in his letters at random; as may feem to fome to have been the cafe, except in one

pretty

pretty long one of his to Addifon, to whom he confeffes an inclination to fhew off. I believe women of education more ready at their pen, as well as tongue, than men. Lady Mary Wortley Montague's letters are written with exemplary fluency and careleffnefs.

" —But having afterwards difcovered, " or been fhewn, that the *truth* which fub- " fifted *in fpite of reafon* could not be very " *clear.*"—

On this a *certain allufion* may be readily impofed.

" Croufaz's *Examen de Pyrrhonifme.*"— Fatalifm is indeed a fpecies of fcepticifm ; that is, it may be fo refolved or conftrued. The affertion amidft the enormities of the world, that *whatever is, is right*, though our author himfelf, no great metaphyfician, fometimes half-inclined to Mandevillianifm, is contradictory to the fenfes : but *fatalifm* may be taken by the other handle, *and*

whatever

whatever is, is wrong, be equally extracted
from it. Warburton's character, of traits
a kin to Johnson's own, is finely drawn,
exhibiting the fpirit of genius, fervid, active,
fearching, and grafping.

" Pope never afterwards"—What fentiments are thefe? Johnfon, whilft he damps
the fpirit of thofe who would attempt to
mend the manners of the times by expofing
them, attributes the fatires of Pope, though
on the Tory-fide, to vile motives: it is
then reafonable to fuppofe that Johnfon
himfelf had no better for his two tranflations of Juvenal, his Ramblers, &c. But is
it not contradictory to common fenfe, and
the nature of things, to fuppofe that juft
cenfure has no effect, and contributes not
to the accumulated code of human morals *? Indeed it feems that Johnfon was a
ftrange compound of inconfiftency, and had
the fortune to have too much care taken of
his writings left behind him.

* See the Adventurer, No. 137.

" Pope

" Pope confulted the modern writers of
" Latin poetry."

There is a great advantage in an affem-
blage of writers in a language known to all,
like the Latin. Such a fraternity contain
within themfelves a univerfal republic; a
name indeed well applied to letters in general, wherein different countries, ranks
and degrees, lords, women, and plough-
men, are, as in love and death, blended
into one common mafs, tending withal to
political republicanifm.

" He fhould therefore have fuffered the
" pamphlet to flutter and die, without con-
" feffing that it ftung him."

Johnfon, with fenfe too formal, heavy
and phlegmatic for a poet of an high clafs,
wrote one tragedy, *Irene*, which, though
not unpoetical, and though *got up*, as the
term is, with great eclat by his contemned
friend, Garrick, contained fo little of the
vis dramatica, fo little action, and that little
horrible, that it fluttered nine nights, and
then

then died, like Cibber's pamphlet: *illine bæ lacbrymæ*, and his contempt of all players, as well as Cibber, whofe head (to do him juftice) was adorned with laurel, his forehead cafed with brafs, and, as our author would reprefent all players, his heart with ftone. Whenever Johnfon left the beaten track of thought, it was through affectation: as when he affirmed, a perfon who is afraid of any thing, or who goes to bed before midnight, to be a fcoundrel. Be this as it may, he never wrote better than in this acute account of Pope's ill-judged and contrived vengeance againft Cibber.

" Let no man dream of influence beyond " his life." What a remark! though not deftitute of truth, and that perhaps which made our author fo fond of life. Even Charles V. found himfelf dead whilft living; yet Chriftina, whofe geuius was of different caft, was perfonally remembered longer:

" 'Tis all thou art, and all the proud fhall be"—

is a verfe of Pope himfelf.

In

In regard to the want of talents of con-
verfation, faid to have been the cafe with
Dryden, Pope, Addifon, &c. the Duke of
Buckinghamfhire has this line on Pope:

" A good companion, and as firm a friend."

and Pope himfelf has this on Addifon ;—

" Born to converfe, and write, and live with eafe."

One is apt to imagine thefe reports of
thofe ready wits, the offspring of envy ; as
to plague Garrick it was given out, and by
his friend, that he could not put on the
gentleman ; the very ftring together with
his defire of the reputation of dancing, to
which his heart moft vibrated, that which
circum præcordia lufit. Eminent perfons are
fure to be thus tiezed, to have fome ftigma
entailed, fome fpot affixed to their fplendour, that it may not be totally infupport-
able to others, or to themfelves. So Cowley,
the author of the *Miftrefs*, was afraid to
declare his paffion ; and Lord Mansfield, the
oracle of the law, muft be unacquainted
with it as long as he lived. But we fhould
not be too ready to cenfure Johnfon for

want

want of candour ; who, if he reprobated
his own father for his beggary, condemned
Addifon for cafting the dirt of poverty at
the Pretender.

" But the truth is, that fuch were fimple
" friendfhips of the *Golden Age*, and are
" now the friendfhips of children."

Golden Age at laft !—To fee the facred
name of friendfhip treated thus, is monftrous and abominable. Hawkefworth, in
his old age, wrote the introduction to
Cooke's Voyages ; the condemned paffage
of which is no more equivocal than fome of
the maxims inculcated in thefe *Lives*, with
which they are tinged throughout, and
rendered the fchool of that which the world
calls *what's what*, rather than of virtue :
ftill the obfervations on Pope's letters are
in the main, juft ; which yet I like much,
though Gray's are faid to be the beft our
language affords. A few pages after, we
find our author defending the manners of
mankind, on whofe friendlinefs he had been
fo curioufly defcanting, and reprefenting
friendfhip

friendſhip in ſuch colours, that hencefor-
ward none will like the accuſation, but every
ſenſible man will be ambitious of the cha-
raƈter of a hypocrite, a Mandeville, and a
Machiavel. Churls may indeed withdraw
their thoughts from worldly greatneſs,
but wiſe men, who know what's what, are
more forward to be ſlaves. Who can deſcribe the faſcinating charms of the notice
of great fools? The ſun of riches and
grandeur is not leſs dazzling to mortal eyes
than the luminary above; and thoſe who
would avoid its influence, muſt ſcarcely
open their eyes: and if they fly into retire-
ment, it is odds that they ſtill find greatneſs
in ſome ſhape, probably in a focus of oppreſſion, where the inhabitants are too thin
to obſtruƈt its rays. So that ſome are indeed compelled to think of that which they
in truth deſpiſe. Thoſe who think to live
independent and unmoleſted of wealth, the
god of this world, will generally find them-
ſelves miſtaken. Incenſe or ſlavery are the
hecatombs greatneſs exaƈts at its ſhrine,
and the world is ready to make the ſacrifice. Our author who was but partially
acquainted

acquainted with mankind, whom he con-
templated through the medium of fmoke,
too much regarded the greatnefs, as it is
called, of man, whofe fphere of action is
but a point, and whofe life is a fpan, as
really important: though the Heathen phi-
lofophers had told him that nothing is great
the contempt of which is greater; and tho'
Cooper fays, that they whofe ambition is
earthly, are cold and dead in regard to
heavenly; that they who worfhip man have
no room in their fouls for the fhrine of their
Creator, their dull and microfcopic minds
being incapable of any object but *little
greatnefs*. Whether Pope's mind was really
great, is another queftion. Johnfon's was
not, unlefs he was an hypocrite inverfe.
He tells us (p. 158) that " indeed, it muft
" be fome very powerful reafon that can
" drive back to folitude him who has once
" enjoyed the pleafures of fociety." That
is, to induce a perfon to *retire* from the
world as it is man's, into it as it is God's.
Yet our author an adorer of monafteries!—
O Johnfon! thy vulgar notions, and thy
palliatives, pardon me, are to me difgufting.

And

And what was the fociety thou waſt fo fond of? Not that of wits furely; for with " what degree of friendſhip wits might " live, very few were fo much fools as to " enquire." Was it one wherein trifling compliances are fubſtituted for real benefits, and not one virtue refides? Was it a fmooth poliſhed furface, in the vain mirror of which men fmile and fmile and are villains? And I do not implicitly fubfcribe to the affertion, that " of things that ter" minate in human life, the world is the " proper judge; that to defpife its fen" tences, if it were poffible, is not juſt; and " if it were juſt, is not poffible;"—for I am not fure that it is confiſtent with my catechifm. In regard to the pleafures of fociety; humane perfons (and Johnſon was himfelf, in many refpects, eminently fo, a noble quality though exerted in treating beggars with gin) will ſteal a thought from it to the unutterable miferies and calamities of the earth; to difeafe and hunger, rapine and outrage, anguiſh and torments, with which it abounds.

The

The * following pages of ſtrictures on
Pope's character are of another caſt; yet
that geniuſes are " always endeavouring
" more than they can do," ſeems hypothetical; for I believe that writers of genius are ſometimes ſatisfied, charmed, and
enamoured of their productions.

Our author proceeds to deſcribe Pope's
independence and exemption from laureat
drudgery, in a fine vein of pleaſantry; and
" he never exchanged praiſe for money,
" nor opened a ſhop of condolence and
" congratulation," is a ſtroke deſerving of
quotation. But ſurely the aſſertion that
" when Dryden had no pecuniary intereſt,
" he had no further ſolicitude," wants qualification, ſpoken of one ſo really ſenſible
of the worth of poetry and literature: and
" Pope had perhaps the judgment of Dry-
" den," might, ſome may think with more
propriety, have been inverted; however,
the diſcriminative parallel between theſe

* How could he deſpiſe thoſe *whom he lived by pleaſing,*
is grammatically ill expreſſed, being complicated.

two

two poets is excellent, and this and the
critique on *Paradiſe Loſt*, are inferior to no
parts of this biography ; and the parallel
wherein, however, he uſes the epithet *velvet*,
in a manner in which he condemns it in
Gray, is cloſed with a modeſty and deference not very familiar to Johnſon. The
criticiſm on the tranſlation of Homer is alſo
ingenious, and, it may be, found. Homer
may perhaps be ſaid to be rendered by
Pope what he would have rendered himſelf
had he lived in Pope's days: yet Pope may
have carried elegance too far ; and I think
there is an unrivalled Homeric ſimplicity in
the latter part of Dryden's firſt Book ; and
indeed I know not whether after all Addiſon did not ſay rightly, that Tickell has
more of Homer than has Pope. But Johnſon's candour can never hold long ; for he
ſays Pope's, that is, Broome's notes, were
intended to ſwell the ſize of the work.

" That the *Meſſiah* excels the Pollio, is no
" great praiſe, if it be conſidered ‚from
" what original the improvements are de-
" rived."

Does

Does this perfectly agree with the doctrine of our author and the orthodox critics,
that religious fubjects are unadapted to
poetry; from which opinion, however, I
beg leave to diffent? Untruths, our author
has obferved, are apt to lead their broachers
into inconfiftency. What he fays of the
" dignity of *ambition*," concerning the *unfortunate lady*, is a quibble on the word.

" Beauties of this kind" (of adapting the
found to the fenfe) " are commonly fancied;
" and when real, are technical and nuga-
" tory, not to be rejected, and not to be
" follicited."

Verfe itfelf is in a manner technical.—
Johnfon, without any ear, fhould not have
been forward to decide on this point. However, he does not deny an analogy between
the currency of verfe and motion. If he
had I might have filenced him with

" And run upon the *fharp* wind of the North."

" Flies o'er the unbending corn," is heavy
inftead of fwift; but " fkims along the
" main,"

" main," is precipitate ;—fo that the whole
of the line well reprefents one getting up
and then running. In page 187, *there*, or
the like, is wanting at the clofe of a paragraph to complete the fenfe, at " mifchief."

" Perhaps neither Pope nor Boileau, &c."
—Our author is too apt to fet the welfare
of this life in competition with eternity ;
and here inculcates, that the trifling and
whimfical vexations occafioned by women,
are more noxious than the lazinefs, gluttony,
hypocrify and ambition of a fcandalous
clergy. Yet thofe are but the petty occurrences of life ; whereas clerical villainy
faps the foundation of all happinefs here
and hereafter.

Pope's affertion in his letter to Mr.
Bridges is exactly in the fpirit of Johnfon,
that " men never approve of any others'
" fenfe, but as it fquares exactly with their
" own." Still it is to be hoped, that all
candour and patience of truth is not entirely banifhed by felf-conceit.

The

The *Effay on Man* is the doctrine of fatalifm: yet the " way the twig is bent, the
" tree's inclin'd," is a contrary pofition.

If Voltaire's *Candide* feems to bear hard
on the goodnefs of providence, it was perhaps the refult of one extreme begetting
another. Of paradoxes, the former part of
the twenty-fecond verfe of the third chapter of Genefis feems to prefent one; as
the knowledge of good and evil may be
deemed a fortunate circumftance. Yet
may it not be refolved thus? That before their fall, Adam and Eve knew not;
were unacquainted with the mixed condition of the world enfuing thereon; but
had experienced nothing but good, unfophifticated with evil. Or by the *knowledge
of good and evil*, may perhaps be fignified
the *conceit and prefumption of fuch knowledge*.
As to the latter part of this verfe, it is beyond my refolution; for to interpret it,
that mankind, how brutal foever and *like
the beafts that perifh*, will not be immortal;
or that the wicked will not be fo, though a
feemingly defirable thing; and that *many*

M   *are*

are called, but few chosen, with some few other texts, may be understood in such a sense, seems heterodox and rash. And that Mrs. Piozzi's expression of our author's excellence beyond *perishable beings*, is to be so understood, is an idea still more extravagant.

Concerning the acute hypercriticisms on on Pope's *Epitaphs*, which are properly no part of this biography, I will, however, ask how our author knew that " peace to thy " gentle shade," was fiction? and add one or two small remarks.

In the last line of the epitaph on Fenton, the poet says that he

" Thank'd Heaven that he had liv'd, and that he dy'd."

Now Terence tells us not to believe a woman when dead, but has not informed us concerning the credit due to a dead man returning thanks for dying. In criticising that on Sir Isaac Newton, it is discovered that *night* and *light* are too nearly allied.

As

As I am fond of repeating excellence, I am convinced that the reader will not be difpleafed at my fetting down that of Ben. Johnfon, which alone would have rendered him immortal, though the name of the lady is not recited ;—

> Underneath this marble hearfe
> Lies the fubject of all verfe,
> Sydney's fifter, Pembroke's mother.
> Death, e'er thou haft kill'd another,
> Fair and virtuous, good as fhe,
> Time fhall throw his dart at thee.

Of thefe fix lines it is almoft criminal to complain of the conclufion of the fenfe at the third line, the half of the piece. There were originally fix more lines as follows, in the laft of which the thought is fomewhat far fetched :

> Marble piles let no man raife
> To her name; for after days
> Some kind woman, born as fhe,
> Reading this, like Niobe
> Shall turn ftatue, and become
> Both her mourner and her tomb.

To

To anticipate a little: this charming piece puts me in mind of Ambrofe Philips's incomparable tranflation of the two fragments of Sappho, which our biographer has omitted to notice, not becaufe he could not fay any thing good of them, but for the contrary reafon, in conjunction with two others; that the fubject was love, and Philips was a Whig; and of Atterbury's fine tranflation of the third Ode of the fourth Book of Horace, which yet is not faultlefs. The firft line of the fifth ftanza, though very beautiful, is a little defective, in that the emphafis, without fome exertion in reading, falls on *the*. In the firft line of the laft ftanza, *eafe* is evidently ufed, not for the fenfe but rhyme: and to " cygnets " dying accents raife," is, I think, obfcure to thofe unacquainted with the original. The meaning is, that the goddefs can raife the mufic of fifhes to that of dying fwans, which is indeed none at all.

Our author has obferved, that according to Dr. Warton, in his *Effay on the Genius and writings of Pope*, that poet had confulted the

the myſtic writers, a claſs totally different and contradictory to the myſterious; the former being of a mercurial, the latter of a leaden genius. In a conjectural view of the myſtics, I ſhall only add, that as there is a falſe enthuſiaſm and a true, ſo there is probably a falſe myſticiſm and a true; and that reaſon ſhould be the mediator to both, leſt enthuſiaſm ſhould run into extravagance on the one hand, or immaleable orthodoxy into ſluggiſhneſs on the other; and ſimilarly, leſt faith ſhould either run into an allegorical labyrinth, or, on the contrary, be immerſed in a dead letter. I know not whether I myſelf ought to be deemed a myſtic, were I to attribute coincidences not infrequently regarded as plagiariſms, to the agency of inviſible beings, which might poſſibly give riſe to the creation of the Muſes, &c. Certain it is, that writers have been accuſed of ſtealing from authors whom they have never read.

M 3   THOMSON.

THOMSON.

" An enumeration of examples to prove " a pofition which nobody denied, " was from the beginning fuperfluous, and " muft quickly grow difgufting."

True; but was not our author himfelf actuated by difgufting diflike to the very liberty in queftion? at leaft, had not his principles fuch a tendency? It feems certain, that they would never have loofened the fhackles of any tyranny or fuperftition.

" The benevolence of Thomfon was fer-
" vid, but not active. He would give, on
" all occafions, what affiftance his purfe
" would fupply;" (a noble character indeed! and I believe poets may challenge
all mankind for generofity;) " but the of-
" fices of intervention, or folicitation, he
" could not conquer his fluggifhnefs fuffi-
" ciently to perform;"—feems, if we may
believe

believe Mrs. Piozzi, an exact portrait of
of Johnfon himfelf, who likewife feems to
have been like Thomfon, " confcious of
" his own character." And let me obferve, that a perfon cannot be fo much
blamed for a careleffnefs towards others ex-
emplified in his own affairs; that even a
neglect of religion is in fome meafure excufable by that of worldly concerns.

" The gaiety of *Spring*, the fplendour of
" *Summer*, the tranquillity of *Autumn*, and
" the horror of *Winter*." This is fuccinct
and beautiful; and yet the writer of thefe
remarks prefers the horrors of Winter,
efpecially when aggravated by a rough
ocean. It is true, that of the fcenes, fhip-
wrecks are the natural confequence; but
what moment paffes unattended with calamities ?

M 4   WATTS.

WATTS.

CONCERNING Watts's poetry, my opinion agrees with our author's — There is in it, I think, a happy, and sometimes almost incomparable freedom of versification, of spirit, and of piety; and it may be said in his own words, that in his Odes

" A thousand loose Pindaric plumes fly
" scatt'ring down the wind."

Yet they are often too puritanical and tautologous; and I believe all his readers are wearied with his chariot, how well soever hung.

" Such he was as every Christian Church
" would rejoice" (*would have rejoiced*, it should have been) " to have adopted," is so, candid a sentence of the candid account of Watts, that I am inclined to forgive our biographer for some of his harshnesses, moved thereto by the friendly name of Sir

Thomas

Thomas Abney, remembranced by Dr. Gib-
bons. Indeed Johnfon could not long fur-
vive fuch a mental refolution. As to extem-
porary preaching, it is generally tautologous: yet I know not that fome may not
compofe extemporaneoufly better than in
their clofets, as a running water fparkles
more than a ftanding lake. As to the next
paragraph, " He did not endeavour to affift
" his eloquence by any gefticulations; for,
" as no corporeal actions have any corre-
" fpondence with theological truth, he did
" not fee how they could enforce it."

If gefticulation, or any mode elfe, could
convey a zeal for things facred or fpiritual,
and Chriftian humility to the heart of man,
it would, in a perfon of five-foot ftature,
hardly have that effect: but I cannot fuppofe our author ferious in fuggefting, that
moderate gefture, accompanying an oral
vigour, can ever enforce it. Emphafis and
action may have naturally a general effect
in imparting help to thought, the body to
affift the foul, as the foul reciprocally af-
fects the body, by imparting a peculiar un-
accountable.

accountable caſt of appearance to perſons
of reſpective ſtations of life, affecting their
manners partly perhaps by the different
trains of thought current in their minds;
or they may do it even by exciting attention. In the following pages, he commends
Watts's " combating Locke at one time,
" and at another, making a catechiſm for
" children," though he had unluckily re-
prehended Milton for doing the like. But
Watts, though a ſacred poet, was ſomehow
his favourite ; but Milton was not. He
affirms indeed, in regard to ſacred poetry,
that " it is ſufficient for Watts to have done
" better than others, what no man has
" done well." He had alleged juſt before,
that the " paucity of topics of *devotional*
" *poetry* en o:ces perpetual repetition,"
which is in eed not void of truth; and
that the " ſanctity of the matter rejects the
" ornaments of the figurative diction ;" but
he muſt have confeſſed that the Pſalmiſt
and prophets ſeem to have afforded examples to the contrary.

OF

OF COLLINS'S

ODE on the Paffions, which has perhaps obtained as much celebrity as it deferves, nothing is faid. Our author obferves, that this poet clogs his verfes with confonants. And I obferve that *Dyer* makes free with grammar, particularly in rendering neutral or intranfitive verbs, tranfitive.

As to Collins's application to bookfellers, and promifing a verfion of Ariftotle's *poetics:* it is to be lamented that men of genius fhould be reduced to the neceffity of mortgaging their brains, and that fums fo fmall can be taken upon them. Indeed our author lifts the veil too much from the myftery of book-making ; difcrediting it, and rendering it in a manner contemptible.

AS

AS TO SHENSTONE,

JOHNSON's and his mind were fo dia-metrically oppofite, that they were like the elephant and rhinoceros; and in the ftory of the wooden book, Johnfon chofe rather to burlefque learning than to omit fo idle a jeft: neverthelefs, of the two, it muft be admitted, that Shenftone was at leaft as far removed from being a piece of timber as himfelf, who a little refembled King Log. For as to the ftanzas of Shen-ftone, " to which" (fays Johnfone) " if any " mind denies its fympathy, it has no ac-" quaintance with love or nature;"—the reader fhould be informed, that it is faid that he had no perception of their beauty till it was pointed out to him; but whe-ther the fketches exhibited by him for lay-ing out pleafure-grounds were his, I know not. Shenftone brings to mind Tickell's lines addreffed to Addifon:

" Ne'er was to the bow'rs of blifs convey'd
" A purer fpirit, or more welcome fhade."—

A2   which

which however were, I fuppofe, too mytho-
logical for our author. Be that as it might,
the concluding criticifm is really cruel :
but it is beyond the power of Johnfon's
libel on this tender poet, Hammond, Gray,
&c. of his ironical commendation of Addifon, as himfelf has given out, or of any pedagogue's contempt, to deftroy their reputation; although he introduces Gray
with his knotted club to knock down the
gentle Shenftone, to be himfelf knocked
down at laft by our blind Polypheme in
the wantonnefs of his might. He makes
Lyttelton too give him a ftroke, in the
fpirit of him who furnifhed the monkies
with clubs to belabour one another for his
diverfion.

The Doctor, as always, fickens at the idea
of any thing rural. Were it not vain to
argue againft a perfon who poffeffed but
three out of the five fenfes, being deftitute
of that of tafte and fight, one might have
afked him who wrote *London*, whether great
cities do not afford fomething fickening,
distrefling,

diftreffing, or horrible, at every ftep by day
or by night. Too true it is, that the favagenefs of mankind renders rural, as well
as other fcenes, often fickening and odious;
but the fcenes of paftoral may be fuppofed
to be laid in Arcadia, or rather indeed in
fancied Arcadia. But if we will not in this
admit fiction allowed to every kind of
poetry, but infift on truth, ancient, or perhaps fome modern, realities may afford fome
fatisfaction. It may not be impoffible, that
as the belief of the true God has always
been preferved in fome corner of the world,
fo the genuine fimplicity of nature may
have never been quite extinct. But otherwife, the paftoral poet may revert to the
ftate of man before the fall. At all times
grazing flocks are certainly a pleafing fight:
though, in modern times, thofe who deem
themfelves of the better fort, annex, like
the loweft of mankind whom they neverthelefs defpife, no idea of entertainment to
the profpect of them, but fordidnefs: they,
I will not fay, like our biographer, have
not the leaft relifh of nature as it is folely
God's.

God's. If, according to a remark of Pope's, in his effay on paftoral, only the pleafing objects of rural life fhould be prefented to view, that of a fhepherd in Britain at this day has agreeable circumftances. Let one figure to himfelf a fine fpring morning; the fun rifing over a diftant hill, befpangling the wide furrounding lawn with pearl, the harmlefs fmiling flocks cropping it, and the lark finging over his head, whilft perhaps the thoughts of his fair one attunes his own voice to the carrol and the fong. If moreover he has a genius for verfe, or mufic to enter-tain his long leifure, the comparifon with fe-queftered fcenes of Arcadia will not feem prepofterous. But withal, the reader of paftoral, as of romance, may pleafe him-felf with the natural congenial idea of a future immortal ftate, realizing, and more than realizing, the fweet tranquil defcrip-tions of Arcadian and Elyfian vales, or of golden caftles and ivory gates turning to angelic harmony, fuch as it never entered the imagination of poet to conceive. Re-garding the paftoral of romance, as better

than

than paſt, as prophetic of whàt is to come ; of, for ought we know, Paradiſe Re-gained, when the thoughts of the butcher ſhall not mingle with the ſight of the flocks and herds.

YOUNG.

YOUNG.

THIS learned (lawyers are always learned) imitator of Johnſon, has been particularly ſuccefsful in grammatical inverſion and perſonification. Yet his figure of *dipping the pen in poetry*, ſeems broken; he ſhould have ſaid, *into the inkſtand of poetry:* and his ſimile of *ſailing from the ſhore*, ſeems ſpoiled in dreſſing. Inſtead of " it only " appears that the ſhore alſo recedes," it would have been better, *it is the ſame thing as if the ſhore receded.*

From the letter of the Archbiſhop to Dr. Young, it appears, that times were altered in the days of Thomas Secker, from what they were in thoſe of Thomas à Becket. Dr. Young, who, with a genius comprehenſive and ſublime, joined real piety with parade; ſome fire with more ſmoke; ſome ſenſe with much wit; ſome meaning with more fuſtian; and ſome ſmoothneſs with an abundance of rigidneſs; moſt excelled,

N   if

if that may be termed excelling, in amplify-
ing his thoughts, and twifting them into a
thoufand fhapes.

MALLET.

MALLET

S EEMS to have been a miniſterial
tool.

AS

AS TO AKENSIDE,

I SHALL put him off with a remark on the "*idle queftion*," as it is termed by Johnfon, who, himfelf, I think, quibbles in oppofing truth and ridicule one to the other, by miftaking the queftion; whereas truth may lie in either ridicule or feriouf-nefs, is general. Truth is the thing fought, but the queftion is how to find it. More-over, that which is grounded thereon need not fear ridicule; but that which is not, is liable to the probe of fatire, though not indeed of capricious merriment. And with tranflating for the benefit of the unlearned reader—the Latin fcrap applied to him:

Pars minima ift ipfa Puella fui.

To Akenfide's fmooth verfe, not fenfe, we ftoop;
As Mifs is not confpicuous, but her hoop.

GRAY.

GRAY AND LYTTELTON.

THIS biography may be compared to the Catullian *Epigram*, which has its venom diffufed throughout; yet it is fo pointed in its tail, by the feverity exercifed to Lyttelton and Gray, that it has alfo confiderable refemblance to the *Epigram* of Martial.

Lord Lyttelton, who, though once chancellor of the exchequer, could not, according to an affertion in the letters afcribed to his fon, count twenty, was in common with the great Duke of Marlborough, the Earl of Godolphin, his friend Mr. Pitt, Lord Holland, and other apoftates, originally a Tory, and careffed by Swift and that party. By the way, nothing is fo irkfome as the precipitate wrongheadednefs and blindnefs of faction. Who would believe that Lord Mansfield, clamoured againft for being a Tory and Jacobite, to have been placed at the head of the Kings Bench by

N 3 George

George II. in the miniftry of the Duke of
Newcaftle? And here juftice ought to be
done to our author's political ideas, how
much foever exploded, that violent Whigs
are not always ready to grant that liberty
which they claim. On the contrary, their
views are to raife themfelves at the expence
of monarchy ; not to promote inferiors to
a participation of the fame franchifes with
themfelves, but to pull down their fupe-
riors to their own level: whilft none are
fonder of ruling, none are more impatient
of obedience.

To fpeculate a little: It muft be granted
that Gray, for inftance, poffeffed a larger
field of knowledge and of genius than
Lyttleton; and that even leffer Shenftone
poffeffed a fine one ; yet how different their
circumftances?---the one a Lazarus, begging
for the crumbs that fell from the other's
table. It is true, that his Lordfhip, like his
friend Lord Chatham, poffeffed a fhare of
Attic wit, and belonged to the univerfe of
letters, as well as to the world of politics.
But Mr. Pitt's knowledge was much confined

fined to politics, the very reafon of his reaching to fuch eminence in his own country; whilft an extended, diffufed walk of fcience avails little at home, though eventually much more important.

Men who would figure in their own time and country, in preference to lafting and general fame, muft, for the moft part, apply themfelves to that which peculiarly belongs to it; to prefent, local, and municipal concerns, refembling topical medicines and the concentration of a focus, to which abilities, rather than genius, are conducive. Again, of abilities there are two kinds, the one refident in the head, and the other in the forehead: a happy union of which is excellently calculated for parchments and the bar, both hateful to elegant genius, and is that which has raifed many to the fummit of the law, to be remembered no where but in reports, a twelvemonth after their death. Yet perfons of higher genius fhould apply themfelves principally to one fpecies of ftudy. It may not be inviduous to obferve of Mr. Pitt, minor, that

his

his genius is quite different from his father's, and wanted not the chicanery of a
rudimental education in the law to render
him a Jefuit.

But our author's remarks on Gray are
not without fome foundation ; particularly
that his language is encumbered and harfh;
and that his poetry was in a manner the
effect of induftry and perfeverance. The
Bard in particulàr is too artificial as oppofed to natural; involved in complications
of figures, forced with tautologies, diftorted
by inverfions, and disjointed by parenthefes
and full points ; and, to carry on the metaphor, raifed or roughened with fret work
into falfe, or at leaft not true, fublime. The
Progrefs of Poefy, a pretty antique word
defpifed by Johnfon, and even his flighter
pieces have likewife a ftiffnefs to which
Pindar had certainly no recourfe, and from
which Dryden's ode is entirely exempt.
Gray owes much to fcowering, as does Virgil to wire-drawn epithets ; whilft Milton
cramps with hard words and eccentricates
by tranfpofition, (remarkable therefore it
                                    is,

is, that *Paradife Loft* and Young's *Night Thoughts* are read by all forts of people; the former doubtlefs for its extravagance, and the latter for its foothing melancholy,) and Shakefpeare often borders on fuftian, but his thoughts ufua¹ly keep pace with his language. Milton's natural paffages are the beft, and moft refemble Homer; and are thofe which approach neareft to the facred writings, whence his hints are chiefly drawn.

I will add fome diftinct remarks on fome of Gray's pieces, after obferving that he has made very free with the writings of others; and juft mentioning that Johnfon has made *it* the pronoun to *profeffor*.

Profpect of Eton College :—

" The captive linnet which enthrall?"

is tautologous: and furely " Gay hope— " poffeft" favours of nonfenfe, though the object of hope may indeed be poffeffed. In the *Progrefs of Poetry*:—Should not " Glory " purfue" be rather *Glory purfues?* Of the
Bard,

Bard, the fourteenth line would be far better, *Cried Mortimer to arms,*—than " To " arms cried Mortimer"—which is very lame.

" Struck the deep forrows of his lyre,"

is a harſh, laboured complication of figures, and there is a further jumble of *ſtriking with a maſter's fire.* *Struck his deeply forrowing lyre* would be folemn, yet fimple. It may be obſerved, that what owes its beauty to contrivance, often appears to be without it, the texture of the workmanſhip being leſs viſible in a poliſhed than an unpoliſhed work. " He reſts among the dead" does not accord with the tenor of the text.

" Heard ye the din of battle bray?"

is rather an odd queſtion. A battle may be figuratively faid to bray; but *din of battles braying,* the *braying* of the *braying,* is a cu-rious *aſſiſm.* And *he,* in the laſt line, is fu-perfluous, inſerted to fill the meaſure. Of the *Fatal Siſters,* the third and fourth ſtanzas would be better if tranſpoſed. In
the

the *Fragment*, *hiding* and *riding* fpoil the uniformity of the metre.

In the firft ftanza of the *Elegy*, he talks of darknefs, and in the third it is moonlight; indeed fhe might have rifen in the mean time. In the feventh, *yielding to the fickle*, is but a poor expreffion; and the furrow itfelf is the broken earth. The twelfth is very excellent. In the twenty-firft "*fpelt* " by the unletter'd Mufe" favours of a bull; and " peep of dawn" in the twenty-fecond, of burlefque, into which " bubbles" in the following one might be alfo conftrued.

As to " the character of the Elegy," Johnfon rejoices " to concur with the com-
" mon reader; for," adds he, " by the
" common fenfe of readers uncorrupted
" with literary prejudices, after all the re-
" finements of fubtlety and the dogmatifm
" of learning, muft be finally decided all
" claim to poetical honours." To which may be added, that all worldly altercations will then ceafe, and that the mould of the church-yard will fatisfy us with earth, a
contemplation

contemplation odious to its fordid fons, who abhor nothing fo much as the thoughts of any thing above it. Our author, in avoiding Scylla, founders on Charybdis; is, in cenfuring the moft part of the poetry of Gray, compelled to pafs a panegyric on fome of it, and on fome of Shenftone's. However, I apprehend, a degree at leaft of refinement neceffary to conftitute judgment in poetry; for as to the common people, they have no idea of any compofition but of fun or narrative, and, like boys, prefer the immaturity of trafh to found productions; and yet, as I have obferved, they are fond of Milton's poems, becaufe narrative, and containing wild indigefted ftories.

CONCLUSION.

CONCLUSION.

*T*HESE *Lives*, which furnish the literary of a century, and contain many
good morsels of criticism, &c. may be named
with Plutarch's, on account of the veins of
pleasantry intersperfed ; but if we compare
the numerous apothegms recorded by Plutarch, with the few recited by Johnson, we
shall find our author's greatly superior, and
be apt to conclude that both Plutarch's he-
roes and himself entertained but an indifferent notion of repartee. These two great
biographers also resemble each other in pof-
fessing a considerable spice of the old woman.

The characteristics of Dr. Johnson were
general and extensive classical erudition,
strong sense, and accurate observation ;
which seasoned with dry humour and sly
detraction, rather than Dryden's free, and
Pope's pungent wit, have rendered his claf-
fical erudition equally immortal. Strange,
and

and a pity it was, that with his great qualities, he, or rather his pofthumous editors,
fhould make the world. the confeffor of his
weakneffes, and of his methodifm, com-
mixed as they were with literary butchery
and favagenefs. Indeed his character con-
fifted of contradictions. Though his piety
was great, and he feared not man, but
God, nor any dangers of death, yet he
trembled at the thoughts of it. His piety
was of the kind, that, haughty and arro-
gant as it was, would have held the world
in the fetters of flavery and prieftcraft,
whilft the precepts inculcated in thefe *lives*
run counter both to divinity and chriftian
morality. He thought that every one but
himfelf fhould fubmit to the great, whilft
he defpifed all men but Popes and Kings,
and his father among the reft. As his own
character was inconfiftent, fo his country-
men, nine in ten of whom defpifed his
principles, and nine in ten of the remain-
der his uncouth manner approaching to
favagenefs, though he was enamoured of a
fmooth luxurious age, adored him. So de-
voted was he to the ways of the world,
that

that in this latter work, he, as Bacon fays of Machiavel, taught rather what men do, than what they ought to do, as Bacon himfelf taught by example.

Of his works; though they have little of originality, and his ftyle has a certain atrabilioufnefs, and his tiffue of paragraphs an unpleafing quaintnefs, it muft be confeffed that his Dictionary, *Rambler*, and the two imitative tranflations of Juvenal, &c. are very excellent; and that thefe *Lives of the Englifh Poets* contain a fund of very valuable general criticifm, and that his remarks on Pope's Epitaphs are fingularly acute, and, for the moft part, juft. But the coarfenefs of his conftitution, his vigorous mind being perhaps vitiated or degraded by the grofsnefs of his body, vibrated not to the delicate touches of a Shenftone and a Hammond, nor even to the ftronger hand of a Gray, but gravitated by the weight of that in which it was inclofed to earth. Johnfon's feelings were more ordinary than fine, which indeed accounts for his popularity; more nervous than elevated; and I take

Hawkef-

Hawkefworth to have been at leaft his equal
in fublimity, and that the author of the
Adventurer deferves one hiftory of his life.

Johnfon was in literature what the firft
Pitt was in politics, both being alike rough
and overbearing. And it would, methinks,
be no difagreeable fpeculation for a moment, how fuch violent fpirits would have
afforted on the national theatre? But, as
according to Johnfon, Garrick was mute in
a court of law, and the Lord Chief Juftice
would probably make but an indifferent figure on the ftage, fo it is probable that he,
whofe knowledge much exceeded Pitt's,
would have borne the bell in converfation,
as he eafily did in the company of Chefterfield, but would not have been a match for
either in Parliament ; though it is not likely that he would have brooked total filence,
as did, according to report, the whole
Houfe of Commons, at one period of Chatham's greatnefs. How was it at the club,
of which Charles Fcx and Burke were
members? When the Doctor ridiculed Lord
Mansfield for being the pack-horfe of the
law,

law, he might have remembered that himfelf had been a lexicographical pioneer.

Johnſon ſeldom writes to the fancy; nor
viſibly ironically ſo as to diſcover ſuch a
purpoſe to the reader; but in a continual
jog-trot of didactic, allowing no holiday.
He conſtantly addreſſes himſelf to the un-
derſtanding; makes no excurſions into the
regions of ſpirits, beyond " this viſible di-
" urnal ſphere," nor eſſays knowledge denied to " ears of fleſh and blood ;" nor even
wiſhes to ſtray beyond the walks of mere
modern life, back to the regions of Gothic
fancy. His timid, impalpable, dreary religion permitted him not to expatiate in the
field of hypotheſis and conjecture; reveries, vain, perhaps, yet amuſing; the food of
the ſoul, and a refuge from the miſeries and
calamities of life. Terribly afraid of free-
thinking, though not hoſtile to free-eating,
he immerſed in dogma and ſuperſtition,
fearing to make uſe of reaſon as a mediator
between extremes. He had the anxiety
and yearning of the Pſalmiſt without the joy
and exultation : ſuch as repel from a plea-

O   ſant

fant contemplation of the Deity, and inftead of imparting delight, make men fhrink back from eternity, and exhibit the idea of death terrible ; fuch as pluck away the rofe buds of ideal hope from the hour of the feparation of foul and body, and point it only with thorns. But thefe maladies, and his other defects and faults, candour will partially fet down to his frame of body, ill adapted to a perfect mind, and acknowledge him, with whofe anecdotes the prefs teemed, to have been no inconfiderable perfon, but a great author, notwithftanding his Dictionary is imperfect, his Rambler pompous, his Idler inane, his lives unjuft, his poetry inconfiderable, his learning common, his ideas vulgar, his Irene a child of mediocrity, his genius and wit moderate, his precepts wordly, his politics narrow, and his religion bigoted.

A DREAM.

A DREAM.

AFTER having been occupied in perus-
ing Dr. Warton's *Essay on the genius
and writings of Pope*, and Dr. Johnson's *Lives
of the English Poets*, the comparison I had
made of those two eminent writers, present-
ed to my mind the following vision :—According to my best recollection of the flitting scene, those Doctors, who frequented
the same walk of classic literature, were in
conversation with each other. The reader
needs not to be informed, that in dreams,
neither the preservation of the unities, nor
the avoidance of anachronisms, are to be expected ; and that inconsistencies and contradictions become natural when the soul and
body are in a manner disunited and at variance.

Dr. Warton. Dr. Johnson, I give you joy
of having finished your *Lives.*

Johnson.

Johnson. (*starting*) Sir, you don't imagine I am going to die?

Warton. No; I rather think you have rendered yourself immortal. *The Doctor is still afraid of dying.*

Johnson. Our opinions in many respects agree.

Warton. Aye, we agree in one great point, in our sentiments of mankind, and in reprobating the opinion of those who represent them as proud, selfish, or knavish; as in all my concerns I have met with none such.

Johnson. Envy, malignity, hatred of honesty and virtue, mixture of pride and wantonness, contempt of the humble, and supercilioufnefs to the unfortunate, with the rest of the catalogue numerated by the satirifts, have never fallen in my way, nor do I acquiesce in the cant, that church-men are lazy, or courtiers insincere.

Warton. No, Sir; I dare say that, during
your

your refidence in London, you have rarely feen wealth haughty, or mifery infulted, any more than thofe refident in the country have been witneffes to oppreffion; and it may be affirmed, that cruelty or calloufnefs belong not to mankind;—that, with a few exceptions, all men do as they would be done by; that there hardly exifts an hypocritical patriot, faint, or divine; that a lawyer who prolongs a caufe to the ruin of his client, or guardian who embezzles a ward's property, are monfters which the world never faw, or knows not of even in modern times; fo that I am in great hopes that the Millenium is approaching, or rather returning. *O how glorious were the ancients, their writings and manners! O the Grecian ages!*

Johnfon. We alfo agree in making charitable allowances for the frailty of human nature, and you will teach that the greateft crimes are to be regarded with a favourable eye, fo that " the univerfe may be " bleffed." *O what charming manners and times are the prefent!*

O 3   *Warton.*

Warton. We agree that rough fatire is improper and unpolite, and that the only method of curing vices is to tickle them; not to exafperate the offenders, for I would as foon men on hell to the Houfe of Lords, as write a fevere fatire; and, in fact, whatever mankind are made of, it is highly wrong to propagate unwelcome truths; and, next to Winchefter, I regard diffimulation as the beft fchool.

Johnfon. Sir, you are right; and you plainly fee, that fince my circumftances have been altered, I have retracted my *Juvenal* and *Rambler*, and even half abjured the Pretender.

Warton. Aye, 'twas poor fleeping on a bulk with Savage.

Johnfon. Sir, you would not have gotten a good living by ftickling hard for religion. But we wander from our fubject, which was criticifm. Sir, you and I refemble each other in our perambulations of the walks of literature.

Warton.

Warton. And yet, like other doctors, we differ. You want tafte, Sir.

Johnfon. Sir, you want fenfe.

Warton. Pardon me, Sir, I did not mean to offend you : indeed you have too much fenfe;—I mean too little fancy, and no fublimity of imagination.

Johnfon. Sir, I have more tafte and imagination than you. If you had any at all, you would have difcerned the excellence of Pope's fimile of the Alps in his Effay on Criticifm.

Warton. Pardon me, you have no tafte for the ancients.

Johnfon. Sir, I like a modern dinner better than one dreffed for Heliogabalus.

Warton. I am not fpeaking of their cookery, but of their writings, which ought to be a model to all pofterity. They unite fimplicity with invention, and have ftrength

O 4 without

without point; and do not, I mean the true claſſics, affect ſmartneſs.

Johnſon. Sir, you have no wit, and there-fore decry it; nor any highflown genius, as you would fancy. And where are the etherial imaginations in the greateſt of the ancients, ſuch as we find in Shakeſpeare, and Milton's Miſcellanies? And in ſcience, the ancients were mere idiots. What do you think of the notion of the ſtars being ſtones, ſnatched up into the ſkies, exhibited in that chaos of nonſenſe named *Plutarch's Morals?*

Warton. You, Doctor, are an affected hu-mouriſt, and aim at dryneſs, ſlyneſs, and archneſs: your ideas and morality are de-bauched with vulgarity, which I was aſham-ed of even in the *Adventurer*, wherein, you know Hawkeſworth's province was chiefly novel and romance; mine, criticiſm; and yours, moral obſervations, in which, but not ſo much as in your *Lives*, you rivet in the minds of people worldly regards, which it is always as difficult to wrench from them

as

as their fouls from their bodies: and your ftyle is not a claffic, Attic vein, but patched with wittinefs; for the true import of *Attic wit* is not wittinefs, much lefs witticifm, but rather fimply *Attic thought*, according to Webb in his *Literary Amufements*;—

" Come, Hooker, with thee let me dwell on a phrafe
" Uncorrupted by wit, unambitious of praife:
" Thy language is chafte, without aims or pretence;
" 'Tis a fweetnefs of breath from a foundnefs of fenfe."

Johnfon. Sir, I yield to no man in thefe qualities. But your Englifh patterns of fimplicity, Hooker, Raleigh, and Bacon, have fhrewd fentences; nor are the Scripture-writers, the beft ancients of all, without them. Homer wrote an heroi-comical poem; and his and Virgil's ftaple works are not ftrangers to point. Some falt, fome zeft is requifite. I feafoned my productions, and they fold. And, Sir, let me tell you, your adoration of Paganifm is no honour to Chriftianity. Sir, I am more afhamed of you.

Warton. Homer, though his fpeakers might
naturally

naturally brandifh fometimes the fpear of wit, he was far above modern wittinefs. As to your fling about Paganifm, if you embrace Mahometanifm, why fhould not I Paganifm, Doctor?

Johnfon. Nor did Homer, like you in your Effay on Pope, go out of his way to tell all he knew, a brag of every one that had fpoken to him.

Warton. Nor keep a toad-eater to retail his fcraps. Pardon me, you are a plagiary.

Johnfon. I a plagiary? Gentle fhepherd, tell me where?

Warton. From my Effay on Pope: particularly you copied my critique on the *Dunciad.*

Johnfon. Becaufe you was a *dunce.* But you only anticipated me in my *Lives* what we had talked over; fo that you are in effect the plagiary.

Warton.

Warton. Punning is not arguing. But it is no wonder that a jingler loves puns. I a dunce! I'll fue you for deſtroying my ſchool, and make your ghoſtſhip enter an appearance, as Judge Buller did Lord George Gordon.

Johnſon. Aye, his Lordſhip was too hard for Buller.—Ha, ha, ha! The law is hardly rhyme or reaſon. As to rhymes, Sir, the want of quantities in Engliſh makes rhyme neceſſary, and the redundant ſyllables admitted at the ends of blank lines, deſtroy their uniformity.

Warton. Rhymes and point are fit only for children; and are as much inferiour to blank verſe, as a round peal to the various modulations of changes, or a wilderneſs of ſweets to a parterre; yet blank verſe is not without uniformity.

Johnſon. What were Cicero's puns fit for? Sir, parterres are more ſtriking than ſerpentine walks; and with all your taſte of antiques, rhyme reſembles the Grecian ar-

chitecture,

chitecture; yet both have modulation, and blank verfe the Gothic; and in didactic poetry, rhyme confers a mathematical concifenefs and clearnefs. What more ftriking than the lines of a regiment in equal rank and file?

Warton. That is not denied; but you have no genius nor tafte for the variegated face of nature, and her wild wood-notes, though yourfelf a favage.

Johnfon. A pedagogue talk of genius! Sir, Nature is regular.

Warton. And fo has blank verfe regularity. You are both a pedagogue and a dictionary-maker; no better than a literary pioneer; and withal, according to Horne Tooke, without one qualification for philofophy. Indeed, I believe that Lowth's examples in his little grammar, have contributed to correct writing more than your huge work; but his Lordfhip fares with him no better than you.

Johnfon.

Johnfon. Sir, you talk of Lowth and grammar, who know not that *nor*, not *or*, is the correfpondent of *neither**. As to the dog Tooke, with all his conceit, houfes and fhips have many partitions, though huts and canoes have none; and what has he faid that we did not know before; this would be procruftes?

Warton. Pardon, pardon, Doctor; you know that three quarters of modern language are factitious, or fictitious, though we were all apprifed of many words being fo; but enough of him. The flip you attribute to me might be an error of the prefs, and you confound *as* and *fo.* But what could poffefs you fo capricioufly to abufe together with Gray, Hammond, Ambrofe, Phillips, &c. Prior, who was of your own kidney? But, alas! indeed, the tender pathetic affections of the heart, humane as yours was in many refpects, had no charms for you, no more than had " ftrains of

---

* In Warton's Effay on Pope, we find " They *neither* " feek *or* expect.' And in the fame page, 212, " *Neither* " Spencer *or* Milton."

" higher

" higher mood." Nature's grand features, and imagery of her own picturefque pencil, the tempeft-beaten fhore, the cormorant buffeting with the whiftling howling wind, or the fcreaming eagle, have no charms for you ; you was incapable of fublime reverie, and nearly of love.

Johnfon. Sir, I was in love with Tetty. But what poffeffed yourfelf to decry Hill and Addifon, and to confider thofe as really vermin who were branded in the *Dunciad,* which was by a flirt of wit to annihilate writers, fuch as Quarles and Bentley, who may neverthelefs live as long as its author himfelf? According, Sir, to your boafted tafte, the *Campaigne,* which is devoid of point, is defcriptive and particular, fhould, inftead of being denominated a gazette in rhyme, have received your ftrong approbation: and Aaron Hill was as humane and friendly a man as any living. As to your reprefentation of Addifon, as of a poetical fancy, but unhappy in vefting it in verfe, it is vain and falfe ; his lines, particularly the verfification of his *Rofamond,* which is
enchanting

enchanting and various, being generally harmonious. But his wit, though pleafing and brilliant, wanted the force of that of Pope, and of Juvenal, whom, with Martial, you ſtrangely pretend to defpife. On the contrary, Sir, a ſmooth ſilver knife will never penetrate to the core of vice; but it muſt be the rough edge of more powerful metal, wielded with a ſtrong hand. The tickle of Horace and Addiſon will but make both the reader and offender laugh, and, therefore, they ſeldom more than rallied follies; and indeed a turn-coat and debauchee, like Horace, could do more with an ill grace. Sir, I have not always written my mind.

Warton. We have no turn-coats in thefe days, Doctor; nor many maſters of feraglios.

Johnſon. Sir, I am no turn-coat. I am a Tory, and would not have accepted of a penſion from Whigs; yet if I had kept a feraglio, my ladies ſhould not have been confined; they ſhould have been Whigs.

Warton.

Warton. Ha, ha, ha!—You defend yourfelf againſt the charge well, I muſt confeſs,
againſt the change of your coat. But,
harkee, Doctor ; a great coat is the beſt of
all, ha, ha, ha!

Johnſon. I am glad you have given me a
fample of Horatian at laſt ; but not equal
to your brother's, when he faid a dubb'd
brewer was a Knight of Malta.

Warton. But, Doctor, how came you to
advife the Scotch Lords to become rebels?

Johnſon. Argyle did fo before me, or
made them fo by intercepting their addreſs
to George I. and after he had raiſed them,
laid them ; but the King afterwards found
him out, and deprived him of his commiſ-
fions.

Warton. You ought to be hanged for
what you faid in the Hebrides ; and for faying that George I. cared nothing about his
crown, meaning, that he regarded only his
Hanoverian farm, peſtered by Hanoverian
rats, according to the Jacobite cant.

Johnſon.

Johnfon. And you ought to be whipped, old Efau, for letting Tom feize the butt of fack ;—

> The Doctor, fweet Doctor, is left in the lurch,
> By the dealer in laurel, the dealer in birch.

Ha, ha, ha! Were it not for *ifs* and *buts,* you would have been a poet, ha, ha, ha!

Warton. But you would not.

Johnfon. Sir, I am a better poet than you ; though, becaufe you have been in Italy, you think yourfelf poffeffed of Italian fancy. And it is to be regretted that Tommy, who fo well diftinguifhed Agincourt from Creffi, is not a profeffor of hiftory ; and then you might become laureat, and tickle Georgy's ears inftead of boy's bums, ha, ha, ha!

Warton. (after a paufe.) When I am lau reat, I'll treat you with a glafs of fack, Doctor, to warm you on your bulk, unlefs you fhould prefer gin, and the times were not changed ; but we have agreed that the

P   world

world is always beneficent, and generous to those in need.

Johnson. So far from your deposing him, he'll hardly bear a brother near his throne; and you resemble the relatives of Eastern Princes, yet are a greater despot over children than the Sophi of Persia.

Warton. Sir, *you* forsooth affect to be the Great Turk, though but a poetaster. But don't you know, that birch bears mitres; and that then the head becomes our province, as we can turn our hands to any thing! A cap is better than bays.

Johnson. Sir, a couplet of my Juvenal weighs more than any of your copies of verses.

Warton. The Latins are to the Greeks, what the French are to the Italians, and as you are to Juvenal; all but imitators.

Johnson. Sir, Juvenal was original, unless

lefs Archilochus was his pattern, and my club* was as heavy as Juvenal's; but yours and your brother's pieces are but toys.

Warton. Serioufly indeed, Doctor, neither of us are poets, and if there are any in Europe of the higher order, we muft go, I believe, to the High Dutch, which language is not melted into refined inanity, and to which poetry is, in a manner, new. The Welch were fublime bards.

Johnfon. There is fomething in that. Do you think I have underftood Greek?

Warton. I think that a Greek etymolo-gift, as you have been, could hardly be ig-norant of it. But Garrick, you know, could not play the gentleman; and Lord Mans-field is no great lawyer; and opinion, you know, is everlafting, when once it has ob-tained. Men would die with envy, could

---

* I a little expected that Johnfon would ferve Warton as he did Ofborn, but he only fhook his oaken ftaff at him.

not

not they find fomething with which to teafe eminence.

But, Doctor, I afk your pardon ; I, if not yourfelf, had really forgotten that you are dead. Pray, can you inform me of any circumftances below? or, are ye all free-mafons?

Johnfon. That, Sir, is a very apt comparifon. I remember, that when I was dying, I grafped my *Rambler* in my right hand, which appeared like a fheet anchor, (for death, in its heterogeneoufnefs and inconfiftency, had the refemblance to a dream) ; but my *Lives* I pufhed from me with my l ft, (let not Tommy pun and fay, I could not retain my *life* any longer) ; and as to my dictionary, I thought to have ufed it for a pillow, but Mr. Tooke advifed me to make a fticklog of it and warm myfelf with it, for indeed I was cold. The laft circumftance of this world that I remember, was a ftrange mixture of words and things fwimming before my fight ;

fight*; and the firft of the other was a
wonder, whither I had been conveyed during my fleep.

Warton. How long ago did it feem that
you had died?

Johnfon. A very little while it feemed;
but how long it really was, I know not.
After awaking, as from a fleep, it came
acrofs me that I had been taken prifoner,
and conveyed to Morocco; and conceived
that a perfon who attended me was a Moor,
and in order to foften his rigour, told him
that I was an Englifhman, and a friend to
his Moorifh Majefty. Sir, fays I, I am
Doctor Samuel Johnfon, the greateft man
in the world, except your mafter and Lord
Mansfield. Sir, fays he, grinning a ghaftly
fmile, we fhall be very glad to fee his Lordfhip, who has fent fome mortals here; but
the King of Pruffia fent as many thoufands:
but, added he, we are not Moors. I then

---

* According to the courfe of this account, as it appeared
to me, I have placed only a femicolon between the two
worlds, at the threfhold.

P 3   perceived

perceived that I was dead, and arrived in the fhades below.

Warton. Did you then recollect about the world you had left?

Johnfon. Yes, Sir, the occurrences of my life rufhed on me in a moft lively and forcible view. The good actions I had done, or attempted, gave me ineffable delight, efpecially when I beheld a huge mill into which oppreffors were thrown to be grinded. I recollected again the *Rambler* and my *Devotions* with rapture, and my *Lives* again founded harfh diffonance in my ears, whilft my *Dictionary* and *Irene* were indifferent to me. But my *Politics*, in which I was fincere, gave me fatisfaction; and my penfion, the fruit, partly of them, and partly of my literary labours, gave me no regret, as I thought I deferved hundreds better than did fome others thoufands, as the poor fhared it with me.

Warton. Literature muft be there fuperfeded

feded by intuition. But who was this perfon you was mentioning?

Johnson. Sir, his name was *Curiofi'y*; a
kind of Mercury to Pluto, who, accompanying *Report*, always attends new-comers of
importance in perfon, whilft fome of their
meffengers attend all. *Curiofity* did not
ftand ftill a moment, but put queftions with
rapidity equal to that with which a maid
of honour inquires about a ball or a wed-
ing, whilft *Report* was alike impatient to
run away with the news.

Warton. I fhould have expected that *Fame*
would have attended *you*, Doctor.

Johnson. Sir, he always fends *Report* before. I inquired of *Curiofity* concerning the
ftate of thofe regions, the manners, cuftoms,
policy, diverfions, &c. all which have a near
refemblance with thofe of this world, infomuch that I am convinced of the earth being a colony of thofe regions, and that it
will never revolt from the mother-country,
though there may be fome few difaffected

perfons.

perfons. *Curiofity* informed me, that it was computed by Pluto, who is feldom miftaken in regard to mankind, that were it in their power, they would be as unwilling to overturn his empire, as would the French to deftroy the Englifh fmuggling-towns: however, he muft certainly over-rate his authority on earth, in his calculation that there is not above one ftrictly honeft man in a hundred thoufand, and not above one in a thoufand who goes to public worfhip for the fake of religion; and that he is in great hopes that many fquint towards him.

Warton. But did not you contradict this, who had fo good an opinion of mankind?

Johnfon. I did: but whether I had not fufficiently recovered myfelf to collect my arguments, or however it was, I had but little fuccefs. On my affirming that Pluto was egregioufly vain and miftaken, *Curiofity* put thefe queftions to me:—How many perfons in England would commute, by refigning religion, on condition of being excufed paying tythe? how many gentlemen had
religion

religion nearer their hearts than their
eftates, or their game? and at laft he afked
me if I knew of an honeft man? When I
anfwered haftily, that I knew many of all
thefe, he coolly bade me reckon them up, on
which I faw numbers of mighty good fort
of people flitting before me and vanifhing.
However, they did not all difappear, and I
perceived King George III. remaining. But
vexed to fee the honefty of fuch numbers
come to nothing, I afked him what he
thought of Mr. Hanway and of Mr. How-
ard; on which the infernal dominions feemed to fhake around me, and *Curiofity* faying
fomething about the Man of Rofs, Dr.
Walwyn, a Prebendary of Canterbury, and
the prefent Mr. John Knox, being for a
moment put to a nonplus; I proceeded to
enquire in what diverfions the infernal inhabitants paffed their time? O, fays he,
in cock-throwing, cock-fighting, bull-bait-
ing, and fporting; chiefly fevering the heads
of animals from their bodies, with chifels
difcharged from flat-barrelled guns, their
mode of fhooting. You are hardly aware
how greatly Pluto is gratified, that, next to
wh—g,

wh—g, all the people of Europe's higheft
gratification is to perfecute and deftroy in-
nocent animals; and that even bifhops follow it, and the generality of the clergy do
little elfe. Then I have heard him boaft,
that there are European cooks as expert in
torturing animals as any in his dominions;
and that the flave-trade does his heart good
to think of it; and that the Englifh Eaft
and Weft Indies hold immediately of his
crown. Then again, the Courts of Inquifi-
tion, of Chancery, and the Spiritual Court,
he fays, are his own; and, jokingly fays,
that Charon himfelf is not more bluff than
the prefent Ch———r, nor his watermen
more dilatory than the mafters.

Warton. Did he fay nothing of the dilato-
rinefs of theatrical managers and bookfellers,
when authors wanted money?

Johnfon. Yes, Sir; he faid that Pluto
boafted that bookfellers defpifed learned
men, as all monied men do curates, and lords
do bifhops. But there I was even with
him: I told him that were not fcholars

poor,

poor, they would not write at all; and that
if rich ones were to write at all, it would
be in favour of tyranny and ariftocracy;
that were not the generality of authors beggars, the chief advantage of literature, the
diffemination of liberty and of the equality
of mankind, would be loft: on which my
companion confeffed that Pluto fometimes
fhook his head at obferving, that good feemed fometimes to fpring from evil, and put
on a grave face.

Warton. But it does not follow thence,
that private vices are public benefits, as I
have obferved.

Johnfon. No, Sir: had mankind, free
agent, never fallen, there would have been
no occafion for good to arife out of evil,
nor for intermediate evil; but all would
have been always right in this world, as we
fhould now hope it will be eventually, and
that the prior lapfe of the angels will be
alfo recovered,

Warton. I perceived, Doctor, that your
journey

journey to the Lowlands without your body, has, as might be expected, improved your metaphyfics.

Johnfon. Sir, I was always a metaphyfician.

Warton. And a politician. Let me know fomething about politics.

Johnfon. Ha, ha, ha! You remember Sir Fletcher Norton's and Beckford's fpeeches to the King. Soon after the arrival of the latter below, he, fancying Pluto like a king of this world, got a remonftrance carried up to him, and replied to his Majefty's anfwer; and what do you think was the confequence?

Warton. I am all attention.

Johnfon. Hey, hey! What, what's this? rejoined Pluto, and clapped a hot coal into his mouth; at which, *Caught a Tartar!* *Caught a Tartar!* echoed through all the infernal caverns; ha, ha, ha!

Warton.

Warton. Ha, ha, ha! The Highlands have not furnished Bofwell with fo pleafant an anecdote; ha, ha, ha! Apropos, let me know fomething of the ftate of politics below. If that is Pluto's manner of ferving patriots, I apprehend there are but few.

Johnfon. And they would be equally fcarce in England, had we an Henry VIII. in which cafe they would not be quite fo loquacious, but would more refemble thofe over the water; but as much as I diflike them, I wifh for no Henry VIIIth's, nor Duke of Brunfwick's neither.

Warton. Indeed the Dutch are very ill ufed; for it is certain that the Stadtholder brought his ill ufage partly on himfelf by his ufurping influence, by which the government had been filently undermined, and is now blown up. His lady is very artful; and they indeed fo headftrong and hafty as not to fee the trap laid for them in her pretended journey, much like the Czarina's towards Turkey, whilft the difturbances in

the

the Auftrian Netherlands, and with the
French Parliament, ftrongly contributed to
the triumph of the Stadtholder, and the
plaufible pretence that the patriots were
the tools of France, contributed ftrongly to
it alfo. Indeed the politics of France, by
being in a manner too fuccefsful, have turn-
ed out the reverfe: her intention being probably no more than to embarafs Britain,
by ftirring up diffentions in the Thirteen
American States; not to eftablifh a Protef-
tant independency; and likewife only to
divide the Dutch, to acquire fomething in
the fcramble, whilft, by a peculiar concur-
rence of circumftances, her party and intereft is become annihilate; fo that the event
of the two laft wars, attended with the effufions of rivers of blood, and expenditure
of countlefs millions, has ended in the tranflation of Canada and Louifiana, and the
emancipation of the Thirteen States.

Warton. France might have profited by
Horace's advice, applied to earthly things
in general; *Vitæ fumma brevis fpem nos vetat*
inchoare longham. Even her policy of accu-
mulating

mulating the debts of England will probably fail her, as through the means of the ftock-purchafing fcheme, Englifh credit becomes the better in proportion to its becoming worfe, as more ftock will be bought up and paid off, the lower it be. But the fcheme was unjuft, efpecially to foreigners, who will profit nothing by a reduction of taxes, whilft the fcheme, by raifing the price of ftock, will render the intereft and compound intereft of lefs value in purchafing frefh ftock, as plainly as any proof in arithmetic. And, at the fame time, the debt renders Britain in a manner the mart of the world, and her empire, and the Hanoverian fucceffion, an univerfal concern of other nations. But we wander from our fubject, which was the polity of the regions below. If Pluto is fynonimous with the devil, it is quite impoffible to difcover his qualities from his character on earth; and confequently, thofe who waver in their fentiments towards him, are very excufable in confidering it as hypothetical. How, it may be alleged, can perfons determine concerning one who is termed *devilifh good*,

devilifh

devilish bad; *devilish clever, devilish aukward*; *devilish cunning, devilish foolish,* &c. &c. &c.— Has he any parliaments?

Johnson. Only nominal; for if the members pretend to open their mouths, he immediately claps a coal in it, which he calls *carbonading*, inftead of a fop in fack, as practifed by the King of England, and fome other princes.

Warton. Who is his prime-minifter?

Johnson. Pride, Sir, the fon of the *World,* and elder brother of *Ambition*; whofe influence pervades all the departments of ftate. *Pleafure* has at times prefided at the helm: but, befides that Pluto confiders him as wavering, and has even fufpected his loyalty, his temper is volatile and carelefs; and though his underftanding and judgment are much fuperior, (*Pride* being indeed the emptieft fool exifting, and feeding, like a cameleon, on air,) and his confequence extenfive, it proved much lefs fo than *Pride's:* and though they are in fome
degree

degree reciprocally influenced by each other, *Pride*'s pre-eminence is much greater, particularly on earth, whofe human inhabitants are the moft prepofterous and foolifh beings in the univerfe, as I have now difcovered, infomuch that a confiderable part of the paftime of the infernal inhabitants is to laugh at them, though they fometimes are afhamed to make them an object of their feduction and derifion, they are fo filly and contemptible. But the motive moft prevalent with *Pluto* for maintaining *Pride* in the ftation of premier, is his great influence with the clergy. However, to give the devil his due, underftanding that his fenate were divided into two great parties, that of *Pleafure* and *Pride*, before he determined to place the latter at the helm, to the prejudice of the former, he ordered their refpective beft fpeakers to urge their claims in his prefence, with the declaration, that the enfign of prime minifter, on which *Detur Tetriori** is infcribed, fhould be given to merit. The argumentation on this oc-

* *Be the prize to the moft horrible.*

Q   cafion

cafion lafted a week ; but I am forry that I
am able to gratify you with only a fmall
part of the fpeeches of *Cupid* on the fide of
Pleafure, and of *Fafhion* on the fide of *Pride*.
Cupid, aware of his merit and weight, in
any rational well-meaning affembly, but
knowing that he fhould lofe the caufe in
that, and intending, when it fhould be decided againft his patron, to take wing and
fly to his mother, the planet *Venus*, made
a whimfical requeft, ere he fpoke, that he
might falute Proferpine, who was prefent
with her hufband. But Pluto, who is not
remarkable for good humour, declared, with
a horrible fmile, that, had he not given his
word that free fpeech fhould not be inter-
rupted, he would have carbonaded him ;
for that however he was attached to him at
the time he had feized Proferpine, he
had been fince tired of them both, and
that rational *Pleafure* was the greateft ene-
my to his dominions. Without doubt, this
ungallant farcafm ftung Proferpine, whofe
fate was very fevere, but who, acquainted
with Cupid's intention of paffing to the
planet Venus, meditated an elopement with
him ;

him: and it muſt be ſuppoſed that Pluto's
choler ſomewhat terrified Cupid, bold as he
is on occaſion, yet his fright was not ſo
great as to prevent his ſpeech, which, whilſt
the plumes of his cap, which he held in his
hand and gently waved, wafted fragrance
around, but to which his audience prefer-
ed the ſcent of ſulphur, was ſomewhat to
this effect :—

   " *O ye Infernals,*

  " What wretched folly and ſtupidity
" poſſeſſes you, that ye ſhould forſake the
" banners of *Pleaſure*, under which ye have
" had ſuch eminent ſucceſs with mankind,
" to change them for that of the moſt empty
" and barren of all beings exiſting, *Pride?*
" Say, O ſay! who, ſince the creation of
" the earth, has occaſioned ſo much mi-
" ſery, calamity, and devaſtation thereon,
" as *Pleaſure*, and your humble ſervant?
" Not to go back to Adam and Eve them-
" ſelves, think, think of the ruin brought
" on the choſen Sampſon by Dalilah, and
" how David and Solomon were led aſtray
" by women! Recollect the havock cauſed

" by Helen, whofe name enforces a pun;
" by Thais, and by Cleopatra. Then confi-
" der, O ye Infernals! confider the power
" of luxury to relax virtue; to render men
" carelefs; to induce libertinifm, and irre-
" ligion, and corruption, all, all the off-
" fpring of *Pleafure!* Remember, O re-
" member the exploits of Bloods, Bucks,
" and Damn'd Honeft Fellows! Think,
" think of the brawls, the execrations, the
" quarrels, the bloodfhed, the ruin of con-
" ftitutions, degeneracy of the human race,
" and virulent poifon mixed with their
" blood and become hereditary! Attend,
" O ye Infernals! attend to thefe things,
" and banifh *Pleafure*, the fountain of all
" the ills and evils of human kind, if ye
" can; to adopt the vacant giant *Pride!*
" O ye Infernals! do not the *Flefh* and the
" *Devil* always go together?"

When *Cupid* had ceafed, *Fafhion*, as he is reprefented in the frontifpiece of the New Bath
Guide, and with a fpacious pair of buckles,
and diminutive hat in his hand, which yet
was an overmatch for his brains, rofe with
some

fome difficulty through the weight of club
of hair and filth, and dreſſed with gunpowder in compliment to Pluto, ſpoke to
the following effect:—

    " *O ye Infernals*,

    " Shall *Pleaſure*, trifling, ſhort-lived *Plea-*
" *ſure*, the paſtime of children, and relying
" on ſuch a whimpering advocate as *Cupid*,
" conteſt the favour of his Sulphureous
" Majeſty with the mighty *Pride*, whoſe
" ſtature reaches from hell to earth? Is
" there a prince; is there a lord; is there
" a biſhop; a ſquire; a parſon; a tradeſ-
" man; a farmer; a mechanic; a labourer;
" a chimney-ſweeper; a ſcullion; a perſon
" living on alms, not proud? Is there a
" Chriſtian on earth who does not value
" himſelf on diametrically contradicting the
" firſt principles of his religion? Are not
" the dignified clergy, to a man, devotees
" to *Pride?* It is notorious to the univerſe
" that they are: and though it muſt be
" confeſſed that their temperance and ab-
" ſtemiouſneſs are great, Pluto ſhall never
" be ſo ungrateful as to deny his obliga-

" tions

" tions to them. Yes, when Chriftians be-
" come humble, and Whigs ceafe to tyran-
" nize, then fay there is no truth in the
" devil. *Cupid* vainly talks of the banners
" of *Pleafure*. Afk the great men of the
" world, even thofe the fondeft of *Pleafure,*
" whether they efteemed him of equal im-
" portance with *Pride,* or rather as an
" amufement for an idle hour, or a jackall
" to *Pride,* and his brother *Ambition.* What
" if Love has fometimes added flames to
" Ambition; is not *Pride* the original
" caufe of all calamity and heartburnings
" among human kind? The whiffler, *Cupid,*
" has boafted of the broken conftitutions
" and poifons entailed by luft on mankind :
" and what then ?   Is it not *Pride* that
" takes delight to thwart and counteract
" nature, the real caufe?   Had love, as na-
" ture defigned it, been equal, and not re-
" ftrained by *Pride,* it would never have
" been pent up in a fink of luft, but would,
" like the Nile, have difpenfed pleafure and
" fertility over the earth.   It is *Pride* that,
" together with its companion Folly, and
" your humble fervant, is the root of every
" ill

" ill that awaits the earth. And it is paſt
" a doubt that your good ſenſe, O ye In-
" fernals, will give your decided ſuffrages
" for him who finds employment for you
" all; in which ye will confirm the judg-
" ment of thoſe worthy Britons, a people
" not always acting ſo agreeably to our
" wiſhes, who framed the marriage-act,
" that bitter pill to that wretched urchin
" *Cupid*, who has forſooth told us, that the
" *Fleſb* and the *Devil* always go together;
" but forgot that the *World* is placed firſt."

When *Pride* had ended, the hollow vaults
refounded with his name, and he was immediately inveſted with the enſign of miniſter; whilſt Cupid and Proſerpine waited
for an opportunity of eloping to Venus.

Warton. Doctor, theſe anecdotes are mar-
velloufly entertaining: but as Ulyſſes and
others have brought accounts before from
the infernal regions, ſome concerning the
elopement you mentioned would be ſtill
more original. Proſerpine had indeed of
all young ladies the hardeſt fortune, to be

Q 4   carried

carried off by fuch a vile wretch to regions
of brimftone whilft fhe was gathering a
nofegay; a rape celebrated by Milton in an
Ovidian puerility bordering on a pun, but
with more propriety by Addifon in his
Cato.

Johnfon. And, Sir, you know not that he
compelled her to drink no liquor but
Stygian porter, dafhed, as I underftand,
with Lethe inftead of opium, which he affirms to be more favory than that of the
Thames, which he declares would poifon
him; and that, though he cannot deny his
temporary refidence in London, he could
never perfuade himfelf to tafte it.

Warton. Dear Doctor, I am impatient for
an account of the elopement, it has the air
of fuch a curious novel, or rather romance:
and indeed when a woman's wits are match-
ed with the devil's, there is good fcope for
betting, though it is true that fome of the
more knowing ones furmife that Pluto was
aware of the defign, and, according to the
practice

practice of his crooked politics, indirectly promoted it.

Johnson. It happened that it was in agitation during the American war, a fource of much joy to the lower regions: and it was concerted between Cupid and Proferpine; it being Pluto's cuftom, on the news of any difafter to the Britifh arms, to have a revel, confifting of morrice-dancing, and all kinds of pranks; after which his majefty fmoked his pipe and ate a roll of brimftone fopped in Lethe, by way of a double nightcap; that on the next event of that kind, the defign fhould be put in execution. It was not long, though I know not whether it was General Burgoyne's or Lord Cornwallis's vanquifhment, ere one of thofe events enfued, and Pluto was fo delighted that he invited the morrice-dancers; played himfelf many pranks and feats of deception; fcraped horribly a monftrous bafsviol; ftared and danced a hornpipe in cap and bells; was extremely pleafant and gallant; fwore Proferpine was as handfome as when he firft brought her down; ordered

a roll

a roll of brimftone and Lethe for both himfelf and her, whilft fhe artfully put hers
afide, fubftituting a fugar-roll and wine in
their ftead, and gave the former to Cerberus to lay him to reft, and, when her
hufband fell afleep, fet off with Cupid, who
had been prefent at the ball in difguife
with a curricle and fwans in waiting ;—

> And from the dire abyfs they whirling drove
> To *Venus*, and the lightfome realms of love,

after, according to a traditional computa-
tion, a refidence below of about five thoufand years ; for there are not wanting fome
to affirm, that Proferpine was no other than
Eve, and that Pluto carried off Cupid, who
was fporting by her fide, along with her.

Warton. When Pluto found that fhe was
gone, his rage muft have been prodigious.

Johnfon. It was indeed dreadful, either
real or pretended. He curfed even the
Americans; for anger, like wine and love,
fpeaks the truth, and wifhed they might
live to feel the effects of their folly : uttered

ed dreadful imprecations againſt *Pleaſure*, his late miniſter, and ſwore that if he did not leave hell immediately, he would carbonade him to eternity; but he might have withheld his threat, *Pleaſure*, and his advocate Cupid, now in the character of a page, having already taken a French leave and attended the runaway: curſed Cerberus for a lazy ſleepy hound; ſwore that but one of his three mouths ſhould ever be fed at a time; and that he ſhould never taſte a bit of brimſtone more; removed him from his ſtation of porter, and placed a monſtrous hydra in his ſtead: execrated Proſerpine for a long-legged fair-complexioned bitch, and Cupid for a capering moppeting puppet, and ſwore he would ſet up a hutch-trap for the Cz——a, fetch her down, and have *her* for his wife. He added, that he had always predicted the ruin of himſelf and his dominions from that ſpeckled planet Venus, and that he would purſue and bring them back, were not he afraid of being bound there for a thouſand years, and that they would prove the Millenium; for *Michael* take me, ſays he, if ever there be a
thouſand

thousand years peace on my earth! But,
in truth, says he, I rejoice that *Proserpine*
is gone, and that I have fairly got rid of
her, together with the sorceress *Pleasure*,
and the brat *Cupid*; for, added he, there
has scarcely been a villain living but has,
at one time or other, had his mind softened
by them, so that I have had but few
thorough-bred offspring even on my own
earth; and Michael fetch me if I myself
have always been myself because of them,
d——n me! It is true that the conduct
of mankind, both in word and deed, generally corresponds with my most sanguine
wishes: that their knavery and brutality
keep due pace with the wahton execrations
of their bodies and souls uttered without
number every hour without any visible motive but my gratification: that the mock
laws against the latter, greatly promote
them; and that filthy *Lust* is a very excellent assistant and friend of mine, though
Cupid, as the urchin himself observed, is
quite of another cast. Adds Pluto, it is
not without good reason, I flatter myself,
that, to say nothing of common swearers
and

and Mahometans, many Chriftian magi-
ftrates when they fwear to adminfter juftice
than which nothing is farther from their
intentions; and fovereigns when they direct *Te Deum* to be fung for fuccefs in their
defigns of laying wafte and fubduing kingdoms, fquint towards me.

Warton. I am inclined to think, Doctor,
that, by this time you are lefs attached to
the earth than you was.

Johnfon. Sir, you are right: from what
I have picked up concerning Venus, no
one would return to the earth, where worthy beings are thinner than valuable plants,
and worthlefs thicker than weeds, could he
have the whole.

Warton. Let me here obferve what has
occurred to me, that the univerfe, its vacuum however, muft be neceffarily infinite,
that it is as difficult to fet bounds to it as
to eternity. The creation proper, as it
might be termed, may indeed have bounds;
but

but it is impoffible to conceive, fuppofe
what you may, plenums or vacuums, but
that there muft be ftill one or the other,
ftill fomewhat beyond, carry your imagination whither you will. So that when we
fay God created the world out of nothing,
we perhaps mean that he furnifhed a dark
vacuum with bodies and fubftances of different kinds. Concerning the planets, except the earth, Mofes has acquainted us with
nothing, becaufe he knew nothing. The
ftudy of aftronomy is moft marvellous and
ftupendous, at which the petty affairs of men
hide indeed their diminifhed heads. The
late difcoveries of Mr. Herfchel of volca-
noes in the moon, of the Georgium Sidus,
of its fatellites, and immenfe magnitude
exceeding all the bodies of our planetary
fyftem, are curious and mighty indeed, if
true, and muft render his name immortal.
I hope you will pardon this digreffion.

Johnfon. Pluto, you remember, called *Venus* fpeckled; the reafon of which is, I underftand, that fhe is cafed with a fubftance refembling

sembling marble, but gemmed with different precious stones, the caufe of her bright
appearance, whilst the earth is hardly vifible to her inhabitants. Your phyfiologifts
on earth are extremely ignorant, and without conception of any material fubftance
that could endure hardly the folar heat of
Venus, certainly not of Mercury for an
hour; not of a comet in its perihelion for
a minute, but it would be melted and
calcined into atoms; and yet fome men
have had the prefumption to fet bounds
to the power of Providence. Though the
torrid zone of Venus is, or would be, in-
fufferably hot and uninhabitable to moft
kinds of material beings, yet by a peculiar
concordia difcors, very little analogous to any
with which we are acquainted, the furface of this planet emits from itself a light
and warmth which is counteracted by the
rays of the fun, not totally different from
the extinction of fires by the fun; fo that
by thefe means, combined with the varying effects of different atmofpheres, whilft
the center of the planet is thus corrected,

and

and the heat moderated, the polar regions
have an intrinfic light and heat; the former of which, about equal to twilight, renders a moon not neceffary. And it is very
probable, that Providence, by means of various incomprehenfible modifications, refembling the endlefs variety of other parts
of nature within our cognizance, may have
thus rendered places habitable and com-
fortable. As to fpiritual beings, unaffected
by matter, all extremities either of heat or
cold are probably the fame to them, the
funs themfelves, or the polar circles of the
moft diftant planets.

Though the appearance of the furface of
Venus is thus, it is, notwithftanding, fertile
in endlefs varieties of moft beautiful plants,
as much fuperior to thofe of the warmeft
regions of the earth, as they to thofe of
the Northern. But as the corporeal con-
fiftence of the inhabitants is infinitely more
excellent and refined than that of the inhabitants of earth, whofe depraved nature,
both in mind and body, is really mortify-
ing

ing and difgufting to confiderate and truly
delicate perfons; fo the vegetables of this
planet do not become grofs food, but
fuch as the reader may endeavour to conceive in the idea of ambrofia; much lefs
do the inhabitants eat the flefh of other
animals; fo that I muft own that the ideas
of the ancient heathens were not all contemptible. Correfpondent with the leffer
vegetables, are the trees, which fhooting
up in innumerable forms of variegated
beauty, by the fides of numberlefs fprings
and natural fcuntains rifing through the
marble furface, and fpreading into cryftal
rivers and canals, over which fruits of various gliftening hue hang dangling and
dancing in the mirrour, verify almoft literally,

There filver rivers thro' enamell'd meadows glide,
And golden trees enrich their fide—

whilft the glorious orb of the fun fufpend-
ed like an immenfe furnace, in a clear blue
fky, adorns the fcene with celeftial radi-
ance, diffufing a delightful warmth without

R   fcorching

fcorching heat. This, it is true, is no more than what fome fpots of the earth may prefent, with refembling, but inferior beauty, that portion of paradifaical happinefs which furvived the fall, yet fure of being contaminated with fome alloy annexed to the race of Adam. In this blifsful region, fear, anxiety, ambition, envy, malice, ftrife, and the reft of the baneful crew of tormentors, are unknown. Whilft on earth even artificial good nature, good manners, is, in this polite age, as it is denominated, laid afide, and every perfon is haughty and eager to announce his fcornful importance and the contempt in which he holds others; it is in that planet improved into univerfal complacency and benevolence, and joined with gratitude to the genius of the place to which they afcribe all the bleffings of which their cup is full, whilft the glow of the health of eternal youth dances in their viens flufhed with joy, but not agitated with luft, to whom thefe other lines of Cowley,

Such

Such robes the faints departed wear,
 Woven all with light divine ;
Such their exalted bodies are,
 And with fuch full glory fhine—

are finely applicable.

Warton. Indeed, indeed, Doctor, you will make me hang myfelf, that I may antici-pate thofe happy regions, and enter them a volunteer ;—

" O 'tis too much for man, but let it ne'er be lefs !"

O when, O when fhall we get loofe from this vain world, the abode of guilt and forrow, and from flogging dull boys! I long, I long to tread yon milky way to the bright palace of eternal day! O what, what wonders are above in the vaft abyfs of the fkies, to which man, though grovelling here below in the fhadow of death, is allied! You obferve that the fun hangs over Venus like a mighty furnace; what then muft be its ap-pearance to the inhabitants of Mercury! and what a boiling caldron of fire muft it-felf be! Let us but fancy ourfelves fpiritual

R 2   beings,

beings, feated in a comet at its remoteft diftance from the fun, that appears little larger
than a ftar, whence we fhall by degrees
pafs into its very neighbourhood; what an
aftonifhing contraft! As we travel on, we
furvey the planets becoming vifible by degrees, but at firft cluftering round the fun:
till, advancing, we perceive them at different diftances, and of different fizes; calcu-
late how near we fhall approach to each
of them; perhaps pafs near enough to the
Georgium Sidus, or Jupiter, to be aftonifh-
ed at their ftupendous magnitude, and
perhaps have a glimpfe of fome immenfe
proportionate ftructure on one or other of
them; or near enough to Saturn to difcover the nature of his ring; and at length
fee the fun itfelf become more and more a
tempefiuous billowy boundlefs ocean of fire,
and perhaps rufh fudden into the midft
of it as into a whirlpool, whilft it roars ftill
louder and more dreadful at the acceffion
of new fuel. And ftill perhaps this unfa-
thomable fiery abyfs, prodigious beyond
all conception, may be but one of a million
of

of leſſer ones, inconſiderable in compariſon;
of one a million times larger than any of
theſe, perhaps the throne itſelf of God; for,
in truth, when we ſay the ſecond, third, or
ſeventh heavens, it is but words without
meaning, over our heads or under our feet
being in effect the ſame.

Johnſon. This is fine indeed, at which a
Chriſtmas tavern-fire hides its diminiſhed
head, how ſavory ſoever it uſed to be, and
the excurſions of my *Rambler* were ſmall
in compariſon. One might imagine that
you had taken a trip beforehand into Venus,
and enjoyed a dream there; where dreams
are exquiſite, fraught with viſions of light
ethereal ſleep engendered by ambroſia and
nectar.

Warton. It is probable that, in a country
like that, the inhabitants of which ſeem to
be half ſpiritualized, they have modes of
travelling, far ſuperior to ours on earth.—
Have they balloons?

Johnſon. Yes, Sir: and a ſtory wanders,
that

that *Pleasure, Proserpine,* and *Cupid,* invent-
ed them soon after their arrival, for the
use chiefly of *Proserpine*; *Pleasure* usually
travelling in the air with *Cupid* in his car-
riages drawn by swans, or doves: and
Proserpine imagining that, from her abode
with *Pluto,* she could sustain the heat of
the planet *Mercury,* declared that she would
attempt a journey thither in her balloon.
She accordingly set off one evening, was ab-
sent for a considerable time, and when she
returned gave out, though it was considered
as a forgery, that she had hovered near
enough to get intelligence that Pluto pur-
suing them on their elopement, had mis-
taken *Mercury* for *Venus,* or imagined that
they were gone to *Mercury,* intending to
put him on a wrong scent, and that he
had settled there.

This conversation between the good Doctors made such an impression on me, that,
in my dream, I determined to borrow her
balloon of Proserpine and go up to *Venus*
myself: but no sooner was I arrived in the
the clouds than, entangled among them, I
seemed

feemed to tumble out, headlong, and awoke; fo that I might be faid to miſtake a cloud for Juno. But I had another nap, during which, methought Dr. Johnſon preſented ſomething like the following letter, from a ſpirit of his acquaintance in Mercury, ſomewhat reſembling the Cock-lane ghoſt, as follows :

" DEAR DOCTOR,

" The planet Mercury, my preſent reſi-
" dence, comparable, from its activity to
" the mineral of the ſame name, is far from
" being ſo ill adapted to the habitation
" even of men, as is generally imagined ;
" ſo that you need not ſo grievouſly regret
" your relinquiſhment of dear earth, eſpe-
" cially as I aſſure you of a haunch of ve-
" niſon whenever you ſhall promiſe us a
" viſit. Perhaps you may ſuppoſe that the
" ſun is here amply ſufficient to roaſt it, or
" an ox whole ; but that is not the caſe
" even under the line. For though the ſun
" is not at more than a quarter of the diſ-
" tance

" tance from us that it is from the earth,
" it does not appear larger than a tea-table,
" by reafon of the thinnefs of the atmof-
" phere, and, from the fame caufe, emits
" much lefs heat than might be imagined,
" as you know the mountains of Peru are
" covered with fnow. And thus we un-
" derftand that the appearance of the fun,
" and temperature of the climate in Mars,
" are nearly the fame as of the earth, by
" means of the groffnefs of the atmofphere,
" which retains warmth a long time, like
" water after fun-fet. From Jupiter we
" hear, that his belts are luminous bodies
" imparting heat, whereby alfo the fun is
" multiplied in a manner correfpondent to
" his moons, as in Saturn, it, by means
" of his ring and other apparatus, is re-
" flected and multiplied in a wonderful
" manner. As to the Georgium Sidus,
" we have no poft eftablifhed from thence,
" though it is not to be doubted that his
" apparatus is very great and wonderful, to
" reconcile the prodigious diftance of the
" fun which would appear to human eyes
little

" little more than a ſtar of the firſt magni-
" tude. Of comets, I can neither ſay nor con-
" ceive, it being deemed impracticable for
" mails to reach them, reconcilable with their
" exceſſively unequal diſtance from the ſun:
" only that as Dr. Reid holds Sir Iſaac
" Newton little better than a fool in op-
" tics; ſo his theory is, in regard to comets
" at leaſt, certainly weak, in imagining
" them merely ſet agoing in a vacuum,
" and to have continued their wild courſes
" ever ſince by means of gravitation; which,
" on the contrary, would, were not their
" orbits maintained by an unknown power,
" continuing their impetus, have precipi-
" tated them into the ſun. Again, Sir
" Iſaac's cauſe aſſigned for the tide on the
" part of the globe oppoſite to the moon
" and ſun in conjunction; that the ſea in
" the nadir being leſs attracted than other
" parts, gravitates leſs towards the center
" of the earth, and is conſequently higher,
" is no leſs futile: ſince to ſuch negative
" cauſe equally operating on the ſea on
" the part of the globe over which the ſun
" and moon act in conjunction, their con-

S   " current

" current attraction, a pofitive caufe, or
" caufes, is fuperadded.

" As to the milky way, it may be no
" very wild imagination to fuppofe it to
" be heaven."

F I N I S.

A CATALOGUE

OF

FRENCH AND ITALIAN

BOOKS,

IMPORTED AND SOLD BY

T. HOOKHAM, NEW BOND STREET.

---

1 ABREGÉ de l'Hiftoire de la Franche Maçonherie, avec un Recueil des Chanfons, par un Membre de cet Ordre, 8vo.

2 ——— des Principes de la Grammaire Françoife, par Monf. Reftaut, 12mo. ——— ——— Hamb. 1784

3 ——— de la Grammaire Françoife, par M. de Wailly, 12mo. Paris, 1772, 1778

4 ——— de l'Hiftoire Romaine à l'Ufage des Jeunes Gens, par M. l'Abbé Tailhie, 5 tom. 12mo.

5 ——— de toutes les Sciences, à l'Ufage des Enfans, 12mo. fig. Bruxelles, 1782

6 ——— Chronologique de l'Hiftoire Générale d'Italie, par M. de Saint Marc, 6 tom. 8vo. ——— Paris, 1761

7 Abrégé Chronogique de l'Hiftoire de France, par le Préfident Henault, contenant les Evènements de cette Hiftoire, depuis Clo vis jufq'à Louis XIVth. 3 tom. 8vo. Paris,

8 De l'Adminiftration des Finances de la France, par M. Necker, 3 tom. 12mo. 1785

9 Adéle de Comm, ou Lettres d'une Fille à fon Pere, 4 tom. 12mo. ——— ——— En France. 1772

10 ——— et Théodore, ou Lettres fur l'Education, 3 tom. 12mo. par Mad. la Comtefs de Genlis Maeftricht, 1784

11 Adjumentum Memoriæ Manuale, 12mo. ——— Viennæ,

12 Alphonfe d'Inange, ou le Nouveau Grandifon, 4 tom. 12mo. Londres, 1787

13 Almanach Litteraire, ou Etrennes d'Apollon pour 1788, 12mo.

14 ——— Royal from l'Année 1788, 8vo. calf gilt.

15 Les Amans d'Autrefois, par Mde. le Comteffe de B***, 3 Parties, 12mo. ——— ——— Paris, 1787

16 Les Amants Malheureux, ou le Comte de Comminge, Drame, par M. d'Arnaud, 8vo. ——— ——— Paris, 1769

17 L'Amant Statue, Comedie, 8vo. ——— Paris, 1785

L'Ami

mandie, et Richard fans Peur, fon Fils—de Fortunatus—de Jean de Calais—Les Quatre Fils d'Aymon Hiftoire Heroique, 3 tom. 12mo.

73 Bibliotheque de Campagne, ou Amufemens de l'Efprit et du Coeur, 12 tom. 12mo. avec fig. —— Amft. 1764

74 —————— des Enfans, ou Connoiffances Elementaires et indifpenfables pour les Enfans des Villes et aes Campagnes, 12mo. Geneve, 1787

75 Les Bigarures d'un Citoyen de Geneve, et fes Confeils . épublicains dediés aux Americaines, 2 tom. 8vo. Phila. 1776

76 Bonheur (Du) par M. Deferres de la Tour, 12mo. Lon. 1767

77 Le Bon Sens, ou Idées Naturelles, oppofées aux Idées furnaturelles, 12mo. —— —— Lond. 1786

78 Le Cabinet des Fées, ou Collection Choifies des Contes aes Fées et autres Contes Merveilleux, ornés de fig. 37. 8vo.

79 —————— des Fées, ou Collection Choifie des Contes des Fées, et autres Contes Merveilleux 37 tom. 12mo. ornée de fig. —— —— Geneve, 1785

80 —————— des Fées, et des Genies, par Madame d'Aulnoy, 14 tom. 12mo. avec fig. —— Bruxelles, 1785

81 C. Julii Cefaris Commentarie de Bello Gallico, et Civili, 18mo. —— —— Rothomagi, 1774

82 Camille, ou Lettres de deux filles de ce Siecle, traduites de l'Anglois, 4 tom. 12mo. —— Londres, 1785

83 Caratteres de Monfieur de la Bruyere, 2 tom. 12mo. Par. 1781

84 ———— par Madame de Puifieux, 2 par. 12mo. Lond. 1750

85 ———— de Theophrafte, et de la Bruyere, avec des Notes, par M. Cafte, 4to. —— Paris, 1765

86 Caroline de Lichfield, par Mad. de ***, publiée par la traducteur de Werther, 2 tom. 12mo. —— Liege, 1786

87 Cartwright's Commentary on the Proverbs of Solomon, in Latin, 4to. —— Amft. 1663

88 Catalogue Raifonné des Manufcrits, confervés dans le Bibliotheque, de la Ville, et Republique de Geneve, par Jean Senebier, 8vo. —— —— Geneve. 1779

89 Catechifme de Morale, fpecialement à l'Ufage de la Jeunefe, 12mo. —— —— Bruxelles, 1785

90 Cecile Fille d'Achmet III. Empereur des Turcs, née en 1710, 2 tom. 12mo. —— Conftan. 1788

91 Cécilia, ou Mémoires d'une Heritiere, par l'Auteur d'Eveline, traduits de l'Anglois, 5 tom. 12mo. Maeftricht, 1784

92 Celide, ou Hiftoire de la Marquife de Bliville, 2 parties, 12mo. Paris et Liege, 1776

93 Les Cent Nouvelles Nouvelles de Madame de Gomez, 20 tom. 12mo. —— —— Liege, 1772

94 Les Cent Nouvelles Nouvelles, fuivent les Cent Nouvelles 4 tom. 12mo. ornée de cent fig. en taille douce Colog. 1786

95 Le Chandelle d'Arras, Poeme Heroique en 18 chants, 12mo. Londres, 1784

96 Choix d'Hiftoires Intereffantes, 12mo. —— Paris, 1781

97 Chanfons Choifies, avec les Airs Notés, 6 tom. 12mo. Londres, 1784

98 L4

98 La Chronique Scandaleuse, ou Memoires pour servir à l'Histoire de la Generation presente, 2 tom. 12mo.　　　Paris, 1785

99 La Chronique Scandaleuse, ou Memoires pour servir à Histoire de la Generation presente, 12mo　———　Paris 1787

100 Le Ciel ouvert à tout l'Univers, et l'Enfer Aneanti par Adr. Louis, 8vo.　———　———　Londres, 1782

101 Code Rural, ou Maximes et Reglements, concernants les Biens de Campagne, 2 tom. 12mo.　———　Paris, 1773

102 Collection complete des Œuvres Philosophiques Litteraires, & Dramatiques de M. Diderot, 5 tom. 8vo. fig. Londres, 1773

103 Collection complete des Œuvres de Madame Riccoboni, 9 tom. 12mo.　———　———　Neuchatel, 1784

104 Collection complete des Œuvres de M. de Voltaire, 31 tom. 12mo. avec fig.　———　Geneve, 1773

105 Collections des Costumes Espagnols, anciens & moderns

106 Collection complete des Œuvres de Crébillon Fils, 14 tom 12mo.　———　———　Londres, 1777

107 Collection complete des Œuvres de J. J. Rousseau, 25 tom.　Geneve, 1782

108 *Comedie scelte di Carlo Goldoni Arrocato Venets*, 3 tom. 12mo.　Londra, 1785·

109 Commentaire Historique sur les Œuvres de l'Auteur de Henriade, &c. 8vo.　———　— Basle, 1776

110 Commentaire sur l'Espirt des Loix de Montesquieu, par M. de Voltaire, 8vo.　———　1778

111 Le Compere Mathieu, ou les Bigarrures de l'Esprit Humain, 3 tom. 12mo.　———　———　Londres, 1777

112 Le Compere Mathieu, ou les Bigarrures de l'Esprit Humain, 4 tom. 18mo, avec fig.　———　Malthe, 1776

113 Le Comte de Valmont, ou les Egaremens de le Raison, 5 tom. c. 8vo. fig.　———　———　Paris, 1778

114 Les Confessions d'un Anglois, ou Memoires de Sir Charles Simpson, 2 tom. 12mo.　———　Lousanne, 1786

115 Confessions de Madamoiselle de Mainville, 3 tom. 12mo.

116 Confessions d'un Courtisane devant uu Philosophe, 12mo,　London, 1784

117 Les Confessions de Monf. Emanuel Figaro, ecrites par lui-même, 12mo.　———　———　London, 1776

118 Les Confessions de J. J. Rousseau, suivies de Reveries du Promeneur Solitaire, 2 tom. 12mo.　Geneve, 1782

119 Confidence Philosophique, 2 tom. 12mo. Geneve,　1776

120 Les Confidence d'une Jolie Femme, 2 tom. 12mo. Amst. & Paris, 1775

121 *Il Congresso di Citera del Conte Algarotti*　———　Londra, 1774

122 Le Conservateur, à Bibliotheque Choisie de Litterature, de Morale, et d'Histoire, 2 tom. 12mo.　———　1787

123 Considérations sur les Causes de la Grandeur des Romains, et de leur Decadence, &c. 12mo.　———　Amst. 1776

124 Constitution de l'Angleterre, ou Etat du Gouvernement Anglois, par M. de Lolme, 2 tom. 12mo. Londres, 1785

152 Le Danger d'une Premiere Faute, Histoire Angloise, 12mo,
Londres, 1784

153 Decameron Anglois, ou Recueil des plus jolies Contes traduits
de l'Anglois, par Miss Mary Wouters, 5 tom. 12mo.
Londres, 1783

154 *Il Decamerone di Giovanni Boccaccio* —— Lond. 1774

155 Decameron François, par M. d'Ussieux, 2 tom. 12mo.
Maestricht, 1775

156 La Decouverte de l'Amerique pour l'instruction et l'amusement
des Enfans et des Jeunes Gens, par M. Campe, traduite de
l'Allemand, par M. Junker, 3 tom. 12mo.   Hamb. 1782

157 *Dei Delitti, e Delle Pene,* 12mo.   ——   *Harlem,* 1780

158 Delassements de l'Homme Sensible, ou Anecdotes diverses,
par M. d'Arnaud, tom. 12mo.   ——   Paris, 1786

159 *Delle Rivoluzioni d'Italia, di Carlo Denina,* 4 tom. 8vo. Ven. 1784

160 Dernières Pensées du Roi de Prusse, ecrites de sa Main,
12mo.   ——   ——   Berlin, 1787

161 Description Generale de la Chine, par M. l'Abbe Grosier,
2 tom. 8vo. avec cartes et fig.   ——   Paris, 1787

162 ———— Historique de l'Italie, en forme de Dictionnaire,
2 tom. 8vo. fig.   ——   Haye, 1776

163 ———— Historique et Critique de l'Italie, par M.
l'Abbé Richard, 6 tom. 12mo.   ——   Paris, 1759

164 ———— des Figures du Paysan Perverti, 12mo.

165 ———— et Usage d'un Cabinet de Physique Experimentale,
par M. Sigaud de la Fond, 2 tom. 8vo. fig.   Paris, 1775

166 Le Destruction de la Ligue, ou la Reduction de Paris, 8vo.
Amst. 1782

168 Deux Ages du Goût, et du Genie François, sous Louis XIV.
et sous Louis XV. par M. de la Dixmerie, 12mo. Amst. 1770

169 Les Deux Freres, Comedie, par M. Milcent, 8vo. Paris, 1785

170 Developpement Nouveau de la Partie Elementaire des Ma-
thematiques, prise dans toute son Etendue, par Louis
Bertrand, 2 tom. 4to. avec fig.   ——   Geneve, 1780

171 Les Devoirs de la Religion Chretienne, pour les Enfans de
le Campagne, ou Recueil de Prieres choisies et interessan-
tes, 12mo.   ——   ——   Paris, 1785

172 Le Diable Boiteux, par M. le Sage, 3 tom. 18mo. Lon. 1784

173 ———— par M. le Sage, 2 tom. 1 fig.
Amst. 1785

174 Dialogues entre le Diable Boiteux, et le Diable Borgne, par
M. le Noble, 12mo.   ——   Amst. 1708

175 Dictionnaire de l'Académie Françoise, 2 tom. 4to. Nis. 1786

176 ———— d'Anecdotes, de Traits Singuliers, et Caracte-
ristques, Historiettes, Bons Mots, &c. &c. 2 tom. 12mo.
Paris, 1770

177 ———— abrégé d'Antiquités, pour servir à l'intelligence
de l'Histoire Ancienne, 12mo.   ——   Paris, 1775

178 ———— abrégé pour l'Intelligence des Auteurs Clas-
siques, Grecs, et Latins, contenant la Geographie, l'Histoire

toire, le Fable et les Antiquités tiré du Grand Dictionnaire de M. Sabbathier, 9 tom. 8vo.   Yverdon, 1772

180 Dictionnaire Botanique et Pharmeceutique, 12mo. Pár. 1777

181 Dictionnaire de Chymie, contenant la Théorie et la Pratique de cette Science, par M. Macguer, 3 tom. 8vo. Par. 1778

182 Dictionnaire Comique, Satyrique, Critique, Burlesque, Libre & Proverbial, par P. J. Leroux, 2 tom. 8vo.   à Pampelune, 1786

183 Dictionnaire Domestique Portatif, 3 tom. c. 8vo. Paris, 1784

184 Dictionnaire Geographique Portatif traduit de l'Anglois de Mr. Echard, par M. Vosgien, 2 tom. 8vo. Bruxelles, 1783

185 Dictionnaire Grammatical de la Langue Françoise, 2 tom. 8vo. calf gilt,   ————   ————   Paris, 1786

186 Dictionnaire Historique (Nouveau) par une Societé de Gens de Lettres, 8 tom. 8vo.   ————   à Caen 1786

187 Dictionnaire Italien & Francoise, par le Sieur Veneroni, 2 tom. 4to.   ————   ————   Paris, 1769

188 Dictionnaire des Merveilles de la Nature, par M. A. I. S. D. 2 tom. 8vo.   ————   ————   Paris, 1787

189 Dictionnaire des Monagrammes, Chiffres, Lettres, Initiales, Logographes, Rebus, &c. traduit de l'Allemand de M. Christ, 8vo. avec fig.   ————   Paris, 1767

190 Dictionnaire Raisonné Universel des Arts et Metiers, par M. l'Abbé Jaubert, 5 tom. 8vo.   ————   Paris, 1773

191 Dictionnaire Raisonné Universel d'Histoire Naturelle, par M. Valmont de Bomare, 9 tom. 8vo. —— Paris, 1775

192 Discours sur le Commerce exterieur des Nations de l'Europe, par M. Herrenschwand, 8vo. Londres,   ————   1787

193 Discours sur le Credit Public des Nations de l'Europe, par M. Herrenschwand, 8vo.   ————   Londres, 1787

194 Discours sur l'Histoire Universel, pour expliquer la suite de la Religion & les Changemens des Empires, par Messire Jaques Benigne Bosset, 4 tom. 12mo. Amst. & Leipzig, 1755

195 Discours sur l'Histoire Universelle, &c. &c. par Bossuet, 2 tom. 12mo.   ————   ————   Paris, 1775

196 Dissertation sur la Nature de notre Existence, Analyse Philosophique de Commune, &c. et Reflexions sur l'Etat actuel de l'Europe, par L. S. Baudy, Citoyen de Genéve, 8vo.

197 Dissertation sur les Comparaison des Thermometres, par J. H. Swinden, 8vo.   ————   Amst. 1778

198 Dolbreuse, ou l'Homme du Siecle, raméné à la Verité, par le Sentiment & par la Raison, Histoire Philosophique, par M. Loaisel de Tréogate 2 parties, 8vo. fig. Amst. 1783

199 La Dot, Comedie, 8vo.   ————   ————   Paris, 1785

200 Doutes sur differentes Opinions, reçues dans le Societé, 2 tom. 12mo.   Londres 1784

201 Le Doyen de Killerine, Histoire Morale, 6 parties, 12mo.   à Lille, 1771

202 Le Droit de le Guerre et de le Paix, par Hugues Grotius, nouvelle traduction, par Jean Barbeyrac, 2 tom. 4to.   Leide, 1759

203 Le Dunciade, Poeme, &c. nouvelle edit. 12mo. Lond. 1776
204 Dutens Itinéraire, 8vo ———— Paris,
205 Economie Politique Moderne, Difcours Fondamental fur la
    Population, 8vo, ———— Londres, 1786
206 L'Ecumoire ou Janzae et Neaduné, Hiftoire Japonoife, par
    M. de Crebillon le Fils, 2 tom. cuts, 12mo. à Pekin, 1756
207 Edda, ou Monumens de la Mythologie et de la Poéfie des an-
    ciens Peuples du Nord, par Mr. P. II. Mellet, 12mo.
                            Geneva, 1717
208 Education complête, ou Abrégé de l'Hiftoire Univerfelle par
    Mad. le P. de Béaumont, 3 tom. fmall 12mo. à la
                            Haye, 1777
209 De l'Education Morale des Enfans, par feu M. Gellert,
    Extraite de fes Leçons de Morale, 8vo. Laufanne, 1786
210 Effects des Paffions, des Plaifirs, de l'Education, et de la
    Negociation, c. 8vo. ———— Londres, 1776
211 Les Egaremens du Coeur, et de l'Efprit, ou Memoires de
    M. de Meilcour, par M. de Crebillon, Fils, Macftr. 1783
212 Egaremens de Julie, 2 parties, 12mo. — Londres, 1776
213 Les Egaremens de Julie, 1 tom, c. 8vo. Paris
214 Egaremens d'un Philofophe, ou la Vie du Chev. de St. Albin,
    par M. de St. Clair, 2 tom. 12mo. Paris, 1787
215 Elemens de Agriculture, par M. Duhamel, du Monceau,
    2 tom. 12mo. avec fig. ———— Paris, 1771
216 ———— l' Architecture Civile à l'Ufage des Cavaliers du
    College Royal Théréfin, par le P. J. B. Izzo, 8vo. fig.
                        Vienne, 1772
217 ———— de l'Hiftoire Romaine, —— Vienne, 1772
                        Vienne, 1772
218 ———— l'Hiftoire d'Angleterre, depuis la Conquete des
    Romains, jufqu'au regne de Geo. IId. par M. l'Abbé
    Millot, 3 tom. 12mo. ———— en Suiffe, 1779
219 ———— l'Hiftoire de France, depuis Clovis jufqu'à
    Louis XV. par M. l'Abbé Millot, 3 tom. 12mo. Paris, 1782
220 ———— de l'Hiftoire Gen. Ancien et Moderne, par M.
    d'Abbé Millot, 9 vol. ———— Par. 1782
221 ———— de Mufique, Theorique et Pratique, fuivant les
    Principes de M. Rameau, par M. d'Alembert, 8vo Lyon.
222 ———— de Ffycolagie, ou Leçons Elementaires fur l'Ame
    à l'ufage des Enfans, par J. H. Campe, traduit de l' Alle-
    mand et orneé de fig. 12mo. ———— Geneve, 1785
223 Elite Poefies Fugitives, 5 tom. 12mo.—— Londres, 1769
224 Eloge Hiftorique d'Albert de Haller. 8vo Geneve, 1778
225 Eloge de Marc-Aurele, par M. Thomas, 12mo. Amft. 1775
226 Eloge du Roi de Pruffe, par l'Auteur de l'Effai Général de
    Tactique, 8vo. ———— Londres, 1787
227 Eloges et Difcours Philofophiques, par Voltaire, 8vo.
                        Amst. 1776
228 Emile Corbett, ou les Malheurs d'une Guerre Civile, traduit
    de l'Anglois, 3 tom. 12mo. ———— Londres, 1783
229 Emile, ou de l'Education, par Jean Jacques Rouffeau, 4 tom.
    12mo. ———— ———— Amft. 1762

230 Emilé ou de l'Education, par J. J. Rousseau, 2 tom. 8vo.
fig. ――――― felon le copie de Paris, 1762
231 Entretiens, Drames et Contes Moraux, à l'Usage des Enfans,
par Mad. de la Fite, 2 tom. 12mo. ――――― Haye, 1784
232 Entretiens d'un Jeune Prince, avec son Gouverneur, 4 tom.
12mo. ――――― Londres, 1785
233 Les Entrevues du Pape Ganganelli servant de suite à ses
Lettres, traduit de l'Italien, 12mo. ――― Anvers, 1778
234 L'Epoux par Supercherie, Comedie de M. Boissy, 12mo.
Paris, 1759
235 Des Erreurs & de la Verité, ou les Hommes rappellés au
principe universel de la Science, 2 tom. 8vo. Edin. 1782
236 Errotika Biblion, 8vo. Rome, 1783
237 L'Espion Anglois, ou Correspondance secrete entre Milord
All-Eye et Milord All-Ear, en 10 tom. 12mo. Lon. 1784
238 L'Esprit de l'Encyclopédie, 7 tom. 12mo. Geneve, 1778
239 Esprit de l'Histoire Générale de l'Europe, depuis l'An 476,
jusqu'à la Paix de Westphalie, 8vo. ――――― Londres, 1788
240 L'Esprit de la Ligue, ou Histoire Politique des Trouble de
France pendant les 16 et 17 siecles par M. Anquetil, 3 tom.
12mo. ――――― ――――― Par. 1783
241 De l'Esprit des Loix, par Montesquieu, 4tom. 12mo.
Londres, 1772
242 L'Esprit de Monf. de Marivaux, ou Morceaux choisies de
ses Ouvrages, 8vo ――――― Paris, 1774
243 Esprit, Maximes, et Principes de M. Jean Jacques Rous-
feau de Geneve, 12mo ――――― Neuchatel, 1764
244 Essai sur l'Administration de St. Dominique, par Guillaume
Thomas Raynal, 8vo. ――――― 1785
245 Essais Philosophiques sur les Mœurs de divers Animaux
Etrangers, avec des Observations relatives aux Principes,
& Usages de plusieurs Peuples, 8vo. ――― Paris, 1782
246 Essai sur le Caractere, les Mœurs, et l'Esprit des Femmes dans
les differens siecles, par M. Thomas, 12mo. Paris, 1772
247 Essai sur l'Histoire Generale, et sur les Mœurs et l'Esprit
des Nations, depuis Charlemagne jusqu'à nous Jours, 7 tom.
12mo. ――――― Amst. 1774
248 Les Essais de Michel de Montaigne, 3 tom. 12mo. Amst. 1787
249 Essais de Montaigne, avec les Notes, de M. Coste, 10 tom.
12mo. ――― ――――― Londres, 1769
250 ――― Historiques sur Paris, de Monf. de St. Foix. 7 tom.
12mo, ――――― ――― Paris, 1776
251 Essai sur les Revolutions de la Musique en France, par M. de
Marmontel, 8vo.
252 ―――sur le Vie de Séneque le Philofophe sur ses écrits & sur les
regnes de Claude et Neron, avec des Notes, Haye, 1779
253 Estelle, Roman Pastoral, par M. de Florian, 8vo. Paris, 1788
254 Etat Préfent du Royaume de Portugal, en l'Année 1766, 12mo.
Lausanne, 1773
255 De l'Etude de l'Histoire, à Monseigneur le Prince de Parme,
par Monf. de Mably, 12mo. Maestricht et Par. 1778
256 Etude de la Nature, par Jacques Henri Bernardin de Saint
Pierre, 3 tom. 12mo. avec fig. ――― Par. 1786
257 Etudes

257 Etudes de la Nature, &c. &c. 4 tom. 12mo. avec fig.
Bruxelles, 1788

258 Eugenie et ses Eleves, ou Lettres et Dialogues à la Usage des Jeunes Perfonnes, par Mad. de la Fite, 2 tom. 12mo.
Paris, 1787

259 Examens des Syftèmes de J. J. Rouffeau, de Geneve, et de M. Count de Gebelin, Auteur du Monde Primitif, par un Solitaire, 8vo. ——————— Geneve, 1786

260 L'Exemple et les Paffions, ou Aventures d'un Jeune Homme de Qualité, 2 tom. 12mo. ——————— Londres, 1785

261 Experiences pour fervir à l'Hiftoire de le Generation des Animaux, et des Plantes, par M. l'Abbé Spallenzani, avec une 'Ebauche de l'Hiftoire des Etres Organifés, avant leur Fecondation, par Jean Senebier, 8vo. — Geneve, 1785

262 Experiences fur le Digeftion de l'Homme, et de differentes Efpeces d'Animaux, par M. l'Abbé Spallanzani, avec des Obfervations, par Jean Senebier, 8vo. Geneve, 1783

263 Fables de Mr. Gay, Suivies du Poëme de l'Eventail, le tout traduit de l'Anglois, par Madame de Keralis 12mo.
Paris, 1759

264 *Favole e Novelle del Dottore Lorenzo Pignotti*. 12mo. Londra, 1784

265 Fables et Contes de Gellert, traduits en Vers, par une Femme Aveugle, 8vo. —— Francfort et Leipfic, 1776

266 Felicie-oumes Fredaines, 2 tom. 18mo. —— Amft. 1786

267 La Femme Jaloufe, Comedie, par M. Desforges, 8vo. Paris,

268 Les Femmes comme il convient de les voir, 2 tom. 12mo.
Londres, 1785

269 Filles (les) Pelebies du 17me. fiecle, ou Honi foit qui mal y penfe, 2 vol.

270 Le Fils Naturel, ou les Epreuves de la Vertu, Comedie, avec un Difcours fur la Poefie Dramatique, par M. Diderot, 12mo. —— —— Amft. 1767

271 Les Foibleffes d'une Jolie Femme, ou Memoires de Madame Vilfranc, 12mo ——————— Amft. 1779

272 Les Folies Philofophiques, par un Homme retiré du Monde, 2 parties, 12mo. —— —— — 1784

273 La Folle Journée, ou le Marriage de Figaro, Comedie, par M. de Beaumarchais, 8vo. —— —— 1785

274 Galatée, Roman Paftorale, imité de Corrantes, par M. de Florian, 12mo. fig. ——————— Paris, 1785

275 Galerie de l'Ancienne Cour, ou Memoires & Anecdotes pour fervir à l'Hiftoire des Regnes de Louis XIV et de Louis XV. 3 tom. 12mo. Maeftricht, 1787

276 Le Gazetier Cuiraffé, ou Anecdotes Scandaleufes de la Cour de France, 12mo. fig. —— 1777

277 Germance, ou l'Exces de Delicateffe, Drame, par M. Mis, 8vo. ——————— Paris, 1786

278 *Gerufalemme Liberata di Torquato Taffo*, 2 tom. 12mo. Lond. 1774
——————————— 2 *tom.* 12mo. *Parigi*, 1783

279 *Giornale di un Viaggio da Coftantinopoli in Polonia dell' Abate Ruggiero Guifeppe Bofcovich*, 8vo — *Baffano*, 1784

280 Grammaire des Dames, ou Nouveau Traité d'Ortographe, François, par M. l'Abbé Barthelemy, 8vo. Geneve, 1787

281 La

281 La Grandeur de Dieu, dans les Merveilles de la Nature, Poeme, par M. Dulard, 12mo. ——— Paris, 1775

282 Les Helviennes, ou Lettres Provinciales Philofophiques, 3 tom. 12mo. ——— Amft. 1784

283 La Henriade, avec les Variantes ornée de fig. 12mo. Par. 1787

284 La Henriade, en dix Chants avec le differtation fur la Mort d'Henri IV. par M. de Voltaire, 18mo. Evreux, 1784

285 Herbert, ou Adieu Richeffes, ou les Mariages, 3 tom. 12mo. Edinb. 1788

286 L'Heureux Jeune Homme, Hiftoire Orientale, 2 tom. 12mo. Lond. 1786

287 Hiftoire Ancienne, par M. Rollin, 13 tom. 12mo. Par. 1775

288 ——— d'Agathon, ou Tableau Philofophique des Mœurs de la Grece traduit de l'Allemand de M. Wicland, 4 tom. 12mo. fig. Leide, 1778

289 ——— d'Angleterre. (Nouvelle) depuis la fondation de la Monarchie, jufqu'à la Paix conclue en 1763, par M. P. des Chavanettes, 6 tom. 12mo. ——— Amft. 1765

290 ——— d'Ayder-Ali-Khan, ou Nouveaux Memoires fur l'Inde avec des Notès Hiftoriques, 2 tom. 12mo. Par. 1783

291 ——— d'Eugénie Bedford, ou le Mariage cru Impoffible, par Madame de Malarme, 2 tom. 12mo. Lond. 1784

292 ——— de Guzman d'Alfarache traduite, par M. le Sage, 2 tom. 12mo. avec fig. ——— Maeftricht, 1777

293 ——— Amoureufe des Gaules, par le Comte de Buffi Rabutin, 6 tom. 18mo. ——— Lond. 1780

294 ——— de France depuis l'etabliffement de le Monarchie jufqu'au Regne de Louis XIV. par M. l'Abbé Velly, 22 vols. 12mo. ——— Paris, 1767

295 ——— de France depuis l'etabliffement de la Monarchie jufqu'à Regne de Louis XIV. par M. l'Abbé Velly, 4to. tom. 1, 2, 3, 4, 5, 6 ——— Paris, 1770

296 ——— de François Premier, Roi de France dit le Grand, Roi et le Pere des Lettres, par M. Gaillard, 8 tom. 12mo. Paris, 1769

297 ——— de Geneve, par M. Spon, 4 tom. 12mo. Gen. 1730

298 ——— de Gil Blas de Santillane, par M. le Sage, 5 tom. 18mo. ——— Londres, 1782

299 ——— du Gil Blas de Santillane, par M. le Sage, 4 tom. 12mo. avec fig. ——— Bruxelles, 1756

300 ——— de Agathe de St. Bohaire, 2 vol. Paris, 1769

300 ——— d'Efpagne depuis la Fondation jufqu'àu prefent Regne, 5 vol.

302 ——— de Clariffe Harlowe, traduite de l'Anglois de Richardfon, par M. le Tourneur, 14 tom. 18mo. fig. Gen. 1786

303 ——— de Henri III. Roi de France et de Pologne, par M. l'Abbé de Sauvigny, 8vo. Par. 1787

304 ——— D'Hypolite Comte de Duglafs, par Mad. d'Aulnoy, 2 tom. 12mo. fig. ——— Amft. 1777

305 ——— Impartiale des Evénemens Militaires et Politiques de la derniere Guerre dans les quartre parties du Monde, par, M. le L———, 3 tom. 12mo. ——— Par. 1785

306 Hiftoire

306 Hiſtoire Littéraire de Geneve par Jean Senébier, 8vo.
Geneve, 1786

307 ———— de la Comteſſe de Gondez, ecrite par elle-même,
2 tom. 12mo. ———— ———— Par. 1751

308 ———— de la derniere Guerre, depuis l'an 1756, juſqu'a l'an
1763, 12mo. ———— Berlin, 1768

309 ———— de la Reine Marguerite de Valois, Premiere Femme
du Henri IV. par M. A. Mongez, 8vo. Par. 1777

310 ———— de l'admirable Don Quichotte traduite de l'Eſpagnol
de Michel de Cervantes, 6 tom. 12mo. fig. Lyons, 1781

311 ———— de Mademoiſelle Sara Burgerhart, traduite du Hol-
landois, 4 tom. 12mo. ———— Lauſanne, 1788

312 ———— de Marguerite d'Anjou, Reine d'Angleterre, par
M. l'Abbé Prevoſt, 4 parties, 12mo. — Amſt. 1741

313 ———— le même, en 12mo. ———— Paris, 1784

314 ———— de Miſs Jenny, par Madame Riccoboni, 4 parties,
12mo. ———— ———— Par. 1775

315 ———— de Monſ. le Marquis de Creſſy, par Madame Riccoboni, 12mo. ———— Amſt. 1772

316 ———— des Chevaliers de Malte, par M. l'Abbé Vertot,
5 tom. 12mo. ———— Amſt. 1780

317 ———— des Progres de la Puiſſance Navale de l'Angleterre,
avec obſervations ſur l'Acte de Navigation, &c. 2 tom.
Yverdon, 1782

318 ———— des Revolutions de Corſe depuis ſes Premiers Habitans juſqu'a nos Jours, par M. l'Abbé de Germanes, 3 tom.
12mo. ———— ———— Paris, 1781

319 ———— du Chevalier des Grieux, et de Manon Leſcaut,
1 tom. 12mo. ———— Amſt. 1756

320 ———— du Cardinal de Polignac pour ſervir d'eclairciſſement,
à une partie des Regnes de Louis XIV. et de Louis XV.
2 tom. 12mo. ———— Paris, 1780

321 ———— Naturelle, Générale, et Particuliere, avec la deſcription du Cabinet du Roi, par M. Buffon, 44 tom. 12mo.
avec fig. ———— ———— Paris, 1775

322 ———— d'une Françoſ-Indienne, 2 tom. 12mo. à Surate, 1787

323 ———— d'un Jeune Grec, Conte Moral, traduite de l'Allemand de M. Wieland, 2 parties, 12mo. Leyde, 1777

324 ———— d'une Jeune Lutherieune. par l'Auteur de l'An
Deux Mille Quatre cent Quarant, 8vo. Neuchatel, 1785

325 ———— du Petit Pompée, imitée de l'Ang. 12mo. Lond. 1784

326 ———— du Paraguay, par le Pere Charlevoix, 6 tom. 12mo.
avec planches ———— ———— Paris, 1757

327 ———— du Temps Paſſé, ou les Contes de ma Mere l'Oye,
avec des Moralités, par M. Perrault, François et Anglois,
2 tom. 18mo. avec fig. ———— Lond. 1785

328 ———— du Traité de Weſtphalie, par le Pere Bougeant,
6 tom. 12mo. ———— ———— Paris, 1751

329 Hiſtoriettes du Jour, ou Paris tel qu'il eſt, Ouvrage qui
contient un grand nombre d'Anecdotes, qui n'avaient
jamais été imprimées, recuelli et publié par M. Nougaret,
2 tom. ———— ———— Lond. 1787

330 Hiſtoire

330 Hiftoire et Regne de Louis XI. par Mad. de Luffan, 12mo
Paris, 1755

331 ——— Litteraire des Troubadours, 3 tom. 12mo. Par. 1774

332 ———- Philofophique, et Politique, des Etabliffements, et
du Commerce des Européens, dans les deux Indes, par
Guillaume Thomas Raynal, 10 tom. 8vo. avec cartes et
figures   Geneve, 1783

333 ———- Poëtique tirée des Poëtes François, avec un Dictionnaire Poëtique, 12mo.   ——— Paris, 1786

334 De l'Homme de fes Facultés Intellectuelles et de fon Édu-
cation, Ouvrage Pofthume de M. Helvetius, 3 vol. c. 8vo.

335 Des Hommes tels qu'ils font, et doivent être, 12mo. Lond.

336 Horace (Juvencius's) Latin, 12mo.   ———   1774

337 L'Hypocrite Demafqué, ou Felix et Colombe, 2 tom. 12mo.
Lond. 1786

338 Jaloux fans Amour, Comédie, par M. Imbert, 8vo. Par. 1785

339 Idylles, par M. Berquin, 8vo.   ———   Paris, 1774

340 Idylles ou Contes Champêtres, par Mad. Levefque, 12mo.
Par. 1786

341 Jérufalem Délivrée, nouvelle edition, Italien et François,
5 tom. 12mo.   ———   Par. 1785

342 Jérufalem Délivrée, Poëme Héroique du Taffe, 2 tom,
12mo.   ———   Lille, 1784

343 Les Jefuites de la Maifon Profeffe de Paris en Belle Humeur,
12mo.   ———   Lions, 1761

344 Il Faut Croire à fa Femme, Comédie, par M. Pigault, 8vo.
Paris, 1786

345 Imirce, ou la Fille de la Nature, 12mo.   — Lond. 1776

346 Les Impoftures de l'Hiftoire, 2 tom. 12mo,   Par. 1770

347 Les Incas, ou la Deftruction de l'Empire de Perou, par M.
Marmontel, 2 tom. 12mo.   Neuchatel, 1777

348 ——— ou la Deftruction de l'Empire du Perou, par M.
Marmontel, 2 tom. 8vo.   ———   Paris, 1777

349 L'Incendie du Havre, faite Hiftorique, 8vo.   Paris, 1786

350 L'Inconnue, Hiftoire Véritable, 12mo.   —   1785

351 Inftructions d'un Pere à fes Enfans, fur la Nature, et fur
la Religion, par Abraham Trembley, 2 tom. 8vo. Gen. 1775

352 Inftitutions Militaires de Vegece, 12mo ——— Paris, 1770

353 Inftructions pour les Jeunes Dames, pour fervir de Suite au
Magazin des Adolefcentes, par Mad. le Prince de Beaumont, 4 tom. 12mo.   —   à Leide et à la Haye, 1779

354 L'Intrigue du Cabinet fous Henri IV. et Louis XIII. ter-
minée, par la Fronde, par M. Anquetil, 4 tom. 12mo.
Maeft. 1782

355 Intrigues Hiftoriques et Galantes du Serrail, fous le Regne
de l'Empereur Selim,   tom. 12mo.   Haye, 1762

356 Introduction Générale à l'Etude de la Politique, des Finances,
et du Commerce, par M. de Beaufobre, 3 tom. 12mo.
Geneve, 1771

357 Introduction familiere à la Connoiffance de la Nature, traduit de l'Anglois de M. M. Trimmer, 12mo. Paris, 1787

358 La Jolie Femme, ou la Femme du Jour, 2 tom. 12mo.
Touloufe, 1778

359 Jofeph

359 Joſeph II. traduit de l'Allemand, 8vo. ——— 1787
360 La Jouiſſance de Soi-même, par le Marquis Caraccioli, 12mo.
    Liege, 1771
361 Les Journées Amuſantes, par Madame de Gomez, 8 tom.
    12mo. avec fig. ——— ——— Amſt. 1776
362 Irene Tragédie de M. de Voltaire, 8vo. Paris, 1779
363 Iſman ou la Fataliſme, Hiſtoire Perſanne traduite du Portugais,
    2 tom.
364 L'Iſle Inconnue, ou Memoires du Chevalier des Gaſtines,
    4 tom. 12mo. avec fig. ——— Paris, 1784
365 Iſmene et Tarſis, ou la Colere de Venus, Roman Poétique par
    M. Grainvillle, 12mo. ——— Lond. 1785
366 Julie, ou le Triomphe de la Conſtance, 2 parties, 12mo.
    Lond. 1715
367 Knapton & Sandby's Terence, Latin, 2 vols. 8vo. cuts, large
    paper ——— ——— Lond. 1781
368 Laure ou Lettres de quelques Perſonnes de Suiſſe, 5 vol.
    12mo. ——— ——— Lond. 1785
369 Leçons de l'Hiſtoire ou Lettres d'un Pere à ſon Fils ſur les
    Faits Intereſſans de l'Hiſtoire Univerſelle, tom. 12mo.
    Paris, 1786
370 ——— de Morale, ou Lectures Academiques, faites dans
    l'Univerſité de Leipſick, par feu M. Gellert, traduit de
    l'Allemand, 2 tom. 8vo. — Utrecht & Leipſick, 1775
371 Lecture du Soir, ou Nouvelles Hiſtoriettes en Proſe, 8vo.
    Paris, 1782
372 Lectures Amuſantes, ou Choix varié de Romans, Contes Mo-
    reaux et Anecdotes Hiſtoriques, 4 parties, 12mo. Amſt. 1778
373 ——— pour les Enfans, ou Choix de petits Contes, égale-
    ment propres à les amuſer, et à leur faire aimer la Vertu,
    3 parties, 12mo. ——— ——— Haye, 1778
374 Lectures Variées, ou Bigarrures Litteraires, 8vo. Paris, 1783
375 Lettres à une Princeſſe d'Allemagne, ſur divers Sujets de
    Phyſique, et de Philoſophie, 3 tom. 8vo. fig. Lond. 1775
376 ——— Angloiſes, ou Hiſtoire de Miſs Clariſſe Har-
    lowe, 13 tom. 12mo. avec fig. Rouen, 1782
377 ——— Chinoiſes, par le Marquis D'Argens, 5 tom. 8vo.
378 ——— de Charlotte à Caroline, ſon Amie, pendant ſa liaiſon
    avec Werter, 2 tom. 12mo. ——— Paris, 1786
379 ——— Chinoiſes, Indiennes, et Tartares, à Monſ. Paw, par
    un Benedictin, 8vo. ——— Paris, 1776
380 Des Lettres de Cachet et des Priſons d'Etat, 8vo. Hamb. 1782
381 Lettres de deux Amans Habitans de Lyon, par M. Leonard,
    tom. 12mo. ——— ——— Lon. 1783
382 ——— de Jenny Bleinmore, par M. Monnet, 2 tom. 12mo.
    à Surete, 1787
383 ——— Juives, par Marquis d'Argent, 6 tom. 8vo.
384 ——— de Julie à Eulalie, ou Tableau du Libertinâge de
    Paris, 12mo. ——— ——— Lond. 1785
385 ——— d'Adelaide de Dammartin, Comteſſe de Sancerre, à
    M. le Comte de Nancé, ſon Ami, par Madame Riccoboni,
    12mo. ——— ——— Paris, 1771
    386 Lettres

410 Lettres Remife à Frédéric Guillaume, IId. Roi Régnant de Pruffe le Jour de fon Avénément au Trône par le Comte de Mirabeau, 8vo

411 Lettres fur la Suiffe, addreffé à Madame de M * * *, par un Voyageur François en 1781, avec cartes & plans, 2 tom. 8vo. ——— ——— Geneve, 1783

412 ——— fur l'Egypte, par Mr. Savary, 3 tom. 8vo. Par. 1786

413 ——— fur la Legiflation. ou l'Ordre Legal, Depravé, Retabli et Perpetué, 3 tom. 12mo. Berne 1775

414 ——— fur quelques Parties de la Suiffe, adreffées à Reine de le Grand Bretagne, par Monf. de Luc, 2 tom. 8vo. Par. 1787

415 ——— Taïtiennes, par Mad. de Monbart, 2 tom 12mo. Bruxelles, 1786

416 Les Liaifons Dangereufes, 4 tom. 12mo, Amft. 1784

417 ——— Dangereufes. 2 tom. 8vo. Neuchatel, 1782

419 ——— en Campagne, Memoires tireés du Pere de la Joye ——— ——— au Quartie r-Royal, 1719

420 Liturgie pour les Proteftans de France, 8vo, Amft. 1765

421 Livre des Enfans, traduit de l'Arabe en François, par un Huron, 8vo. Londres, 1783

422 Les Loifirs d'un Miniftre d'Etat ou Effais dans le Gout de ceux de Montaigne, 2 tom ——— Amft. 1787

423 Louife, ou la Chaumière dans les Marais, traduit de l'Anglois, 2 tom. ——— ——— Londres, 1788

424 Luefden's Greek Teftament, 12mo. Amft. 1740

425 Le Lycée de la Jeuneffe, ou les Etudes Reparées, par M. Mouftelon, 2 tom. 12mo. ——— Paris, 1786

426 Ma Converfion, 12mo. ——— à Stamoul, 1783

427 Magafin des Adolefcentes, par Mad. le Prince de Beaumont, 4 tom. 12mo. ——— à Leyde à le Haye, 1777

428 ——— des Enfans, par Mad. le Prince de Beaumont, 4 tom. 12mo ——— à Leide & le Haye, 1777

429 Le Maitre de la Langue Allemande, ou Nouvelle Grammaire Allemande de M. le Prof, Gottfched 8vo. en Souife, 1782

430 Le Maitre Italien dans fa derniere Perfe+on, par le Sieur Veneroni, 12mo. ——— ——— Paris 1784

431 Le Maitre Italien, ou la Grammaire Françoife et Italienne de Veneroni, 8vo. ——— ——— Lyon, 1784

432 Le Maitre Tofcan, ou Nouvelle Methode pour apprendre la Langue Italienne, par Borzacchini, 12mo, Londres, 1776

433 Les Malheurs de l'Amour, 2 tom. 12mo. Amft. 1766

434 Les Malheurs de la l'Inconftance, ou Lettres de la Marquife de Syrce, et du Comte de Mirabelle, 2 tom. 12mo. Rouen 1782

435 De la Maniere d'Ecrire l'Hiftoire, par M. l'Abbé de Mably, 12mo. ——— Paris, 1783

436 La Maniere de Bien Penfer, dans les Ouvrages d'Efprit 12mo. Paris, 1771

437 Manuel d'Epictete, 8vo. ——— Geneve, 1783

439 Marie d'Angleterre Reine Ducheffe, par Mad. de Luffan, 12mo. ——— ——— Amft., 1749

C

440 Le

440 Le Mari Sentimental, ou le Mariage comme il y en à quelques uns, 12mo. ——— Geneve, 1785

441 Marseille Ancienne et Moderne, par Monf. Guys, 8vo. Paris

442 Le Masque de Fer, ou les Avantures Admirables du Pere & du Fils, 2 tom. 12mo. ——— à la Haye, 1777 & 1785

443 La Matinée la soirée, et la Nuit des Boulevards, Ambigu de Scenes Episodiques, 8vo. ——— Paris, 1776

444 Les Matinées Liegeoises, ou l'Art de prendre le Thé, en s'amusant, 2 tom. 12mo. ——— Liege, 1778

445 *Il Mettino, Il Mezzodi, le Sere, e la Notte del original tedesco di Frederico Guglielmo Zaccaria*, 8vo. ——— Bassano,

446 Mauback's Natural Method of teaching and learning the French Language, French and English, 8vo. London,

447 Mâlanges de Litterature Orientale, traduits de diffe ens Manuscripts Turcs, Arabes, & Persans, par M. Cardonne, 2 tom. 12mo. ——— ——— Paris, 1770

448 Memoire au Roi, par M. Linguet, concernant ses Reclamations actuellement pendantes au Parlement de Paris, 8vo. Lond. 1786

449 ——— d'Anne de Gonzagues, Princesse Paletine, 8vo. Lond. 1786

450 ——— de Gaudence de Lucques, Prisonnier de l'Inquisition, 4 tom. 12mo. fig. ——— Amst. & Liege, 1777

451 ——— de Grammont, 2 tom. 18mo., par le C. Antoine Hamilton, ——— ——— 1776

452 ——— de Guy Jolie, pour servir de suite aux memoires du Cardinal de Retz, tom. 12mo. ——— Geneve, 1779

453 ——— de l'Abbé Terrai, Controlleur General des Finances, 12mo. ——— Lond. 1775

454 ——— de Madame le Baronne de Batteville, ou la Veuve Parfaite, par Madame le Prince de Beaumont, 12mo.

455 ——— de Mademoiselle de Montpensier, Fille de Gaston, d'Orleans, pere de Louis XIII. Roi de France, 8tom. 12mo. Maest. 1776

456 ——— de Mademoiselle de Sternheim, publiés, par M. Wieland, et traduit de l'Allemand, par Madame * * *, 2 tom, ——— Haye, 1775

457 ——— de Madame de Warens, suivis de ceux de Claude Anet, 12mo. ——— Chamborg, 1786

458 ——— de M, de Voltaire, ecrits par lui-même, 12mo.

459 ——— de M. Goldoni, pour servir à l'Histoire de sa Vie, et à celle de son Théatre, 3 tom. 8vo. ——— Paris 1787

460 ——— de Montecuculi, Generalissime des Troupes de l'Empereur, avec fig. 12mo. ——— Paris, 1760

461 ——— de Montecuculi, Generalissime des Armés de l'Empereur, avec les Commentaires de M. le Comte Turpin de Caissé, 3 tom. 8vo. avec fig. Amst. et Leipzig, 1770

463 ———, de Maximilien de Bethune Duc de Sully, Ministre de Henri XIV. 10 tom. 12 mo. ——— Londres, 1778

464 Memoires

464 Memoires de Rigobert Zapata, par M. de Lignec, 2 tom.
12 mo. — — — Lille, 1780

465 ———— de Sir George Wollap, fes Voyages dans differentes
parties du Monde, Aventures Extraordinaires qui lui ar-
rivent, &c. &c. 3 tom. 12mo. ———— Lond. 1784

466 ————de Verforand, 2 tom. 12mo. — Maeft. 1774

467 ————de Baron de Tott, fur les Turc, et les Tartares,
4 tom. 12mo. — — Maeft. 1785

468 ———— de Baron de Tott, fur les Turcs, et les Tartares,

469 ———— du Cardinal de Retz, et de Guy Joli, 6 tom. 12mo.

470 ————du Cardinal de Retz, 4 tom. 12mo. Geneve, 1779

471 ———— du Maréchal de Berwick, ecrits par lui-même,
2 tom. 12mo. — — — Paris, 1778

472 ———— du Chevalier de Ravanne, Page de S. A R. le Duc
Regent, et Moufquetaire, 3 tom. 12mo. Amft. 1755

473 Memoires et Lettres de Madame de Maintenon, par M. de
Beaumelle, 16 tom. — — Maeft. 1778

474 ———— Militaires, fur les Grecs, et les Romains pour fervir
de fuite & d'clairciffement aux Commentaires du Chevalier
Folàld fur l'Hiftoire de Polybe, 9 tom. 4to. fig. wants
titles

475 ————et Reflexions fur les principaux Evénemens du
Regne de Louis XIV. par L. M. D. L. F. 12mo. Am. 1755

476 ———— Hiftoriques, Critiques, et Anecdotes des Reines,
et Regentes de France, 6 tom. 12mo. — Amft. 1776

477 ———— Hiftoriques, & Politiques, des Pays–Bas Autri-
chiens, 8vo. ———— ———— Neuchatel, 1784

478 ———— pour fervir à la Connoiffance des Affaires Politiques,
et Economiques, du Royaume de Suéde, jufqu'à le fin de
la 1775me Année, tom. 2de. 4to. avec fig. et tables,
Londres, 1776

479 ———— pour fervir à l'Hiftoire d'Anne d'Autriche, Epoufe
de Louis XIII. Roi de France, par Madame de Mottéville,
6 tom. 12mo. — — Maeft. 1782

480 ———— Politiques et Militaires, pour fervir à l'Hiftoire de
Louis XIV. et de Louis XV. compofé fur les Pieces Originales recueillies, par M. le Duc de Noailles, Maréchal de
France, and Miniftre d'Etat, par l'Abbé Millot, 6 tom.
12mo. — — Paris, 1777

481 ———— Secretes pour fervir à l'Hiftoire de la Republique
des Lettres en France, depuis 1762, jufqu'à nos Jours, ou
Journal d'un Obfervateur, par feu M. de Bachaumont,
23 tom. 12mo. Londres, 1781, &c.

482 ———— fur la Vie et Lettres de Mad. Ninon de l'Enclos

483 ———— fur l'Electricité et le Magnétifme, par J. H. Van
Swinden, 3 tom. 8vo. fig. Haye, 1785

484 ———— fur le Mariage des Proteftans en 1785, 8vo. Lond.
———————— (fecond) fur le même, 8vo Lon. 1787

485 ———— fur les Samofedes et les Lappons, Copenhag. 1766

486 Mentor Moderne, ou Inftructions pour les Garçons, et pour
ceux qui les élevent, par Mad. de Beaumont. 12 tom. 12mo.
Paris, 1776

487 Les Méprifes, ou Lettres du Comte d'Arabel, 12mo.

488 Mercuré de Vittoris Siri, contenant l'Hiftoire Générale de l'Europe, depuis 1640 jufqu'à 5655, traduit de l'Italien, par M. Requier, 18 tom. 12mo. —— Paris, 1759

489 Les Merveilles du Ciel, et de l'Enfer, et des Terres Plané-taires et Aftrales, traduit du Latin de Emmanuel de Sweden-borg, 2 tom. 8vo. —— Berlin, 1782

490 Les Metamorphofes d'Ovide en Vers Francois, per M. de Saint Ange, c. 8vo. —— —— —— Paris, 1785

491 Methode Abrégée & Facile, pour apprendre la Geographie,

492 Les Mille et Une Faveurs, Contes de Cour, tirés de l'Ancien Gaulois, par la Reine de Navarre, 5 tom. 12mo. Lond.

493 —————— et une Folies, Contes Français, par M. N * * *, 4 tom. 12mo. —— —— Amft. & Paris, 1771

494 —————— et une Heures Contes Peruviennes

495 —————— et une Nuits, Contes Arabs, traduits en François par M. Gelland, 8 tom. 12mo. —— Paris, 1773

496 —————— et une Soirées, Contes Mogols, 3 tom. 12mo. Lille, 1782

497 *La Litologia, e le Favole Spiegate colla Storia opera dell A. B. Bancieer, 4 tom 12no. fig.* —— *Napol,* 1754

498 Les Moeurs, 3 parties, 12mo. —— 1784

499 Mon Bonnet de Nuit, par M. Mercier, tom. 1, 2. 8vo. Neuchatel, 1784

500 Mon Elêve, ou Emile Inftituteur, nouvelle Education Mo-rale, 8vo. Aux Verrieres Suiffes —— 1786

501 Le Monde fon Origine, et fon Antiquité, de l'Ame, et de fon Immortalité, Éffai fur la Chronologie, 8vo.

502 Monfieur Guillaume ou le Difputeur, 8vo. Lond. 1781

503 La Morale Evangélique, ou Difcours fur le Sermon de Jefus Chrift fur la Montagne, 7 tom. 8vo. Neuch. 1778

504 Morceaux choifies de Tacite, traduits en François, avec le Latin à coté, par M. d'Allembert,, 2 tom. 12mo. Paris.

505 *La Morte d'Abelle, Poema tedefco del Sig. Geffner, tradotto del Sig. Abate Mugnozzi,* 12mo. —— *Parigi,* 1782

506 La Mouche, ou les Aventures de M. Bigand, traduites de l'Italien, par la Chevalier de Mouchy, 4 tom. 12mo. Amft. 1737

507 Le Moyen de Parvenir, 2 tom. 12mo. — 1000, 700, 73

508 *Le Notti di Young, tradotte dall' Inglefe, e dal Francefe, dal Sig-nor Abbate Alberti,* 2 tom. 12mo. —— *Marfiglia,* 1770

509 Nouvelle Atlas des Enfans, ou Principes pour apprendre fa-cilement la Geographie, enrichi de 24 Cartes enluminees, 12mo. —— —— Amft. 1782

510 Nouveaux Contes Turcs, et Arabes, traduits de l'Arabe, et du Turc, par M. Digeon, 2 tom. Bruxelles, 1781

511 Nouveau Memoire fur l'Ouverture de l'Efcaut, par M. Lin-guet, 8vo —— —— Bruxelles, 1785

512 Le Nouveau Newkaftle, ou Nouveau traité de Cavalerie, 12mo. —— —— Lyon, 1771

513 Nouveau

513 Nouveau Precis de l'Hiſtoire d'Angleterre traduit de l'Anglois, 12mo. ——— ——— Paris, 1785

514 Nouveau Voyage à la Mer du Sud, par M. Marion Ducleſmeur, Caozet et de Surville, 8vo. ——— Paris, 1783

515 ——— Werther, imité de l'Allemand, 8vo. Neuch. 1786

516 Nouvel Abrégé Chronologique de l'Hiſtoire de Françe, 3 parties, 12mo. ——— ——— Paris. 1774

517 Nouvel Abrégé de l'Hiſtoire de France, à l'Uſage des Jeunes Gens, par Mad. d'Eſpinaſſy, 3 tom. 12mo. Paris, 1767

518 Nouvelles Decouvertes des Ruſſes, entre l'Aſie, et l'Amerique, avec l'Hiſtoire de la Conquete de la Siberie, et du Commerce du Ruſſes, et des Chinois, traduit de l'Anglois, de M. Coxe, 8vo. Neuch. 1781

519 Nouvelle Deſcription des Glacieres, Valleés de Glace, et Glaciers qui forment la grande Chäine des Alpes des Suiſſe, d'Italie et de Savoye, par M. Bourrit, 3 tom. 8vo. avec fig. ——— ——— Geneve, 1785--87

520 Nouvelles Eſpagnolles, traduites, par M. d'Uſſieux, 2 tom. 12mo. ——— Madrid & Paris, 1778

521 Nouvelle Grammaire Univerſelle Eſpagnolle, et Françoiſe, compoſée par M. Antoine Galmace, et augmentée des additions du Rev. Pere Nunez, 8vo. Paris, 1775

522 La Nouvelle Heloïſe, ou Lettres des Deux Amans, &c. &c. 4 tom. 12mo. ——— ——— Geneve, 1780

523 ——— Heloïſe, &c. 3 tom. avec fig. Geneve, 1783

524 ——— Heloïſe, ou Lettres de deux Amants, par J. J. Rouſſeau, 6 tom. 12mo. fig. ——— Geneve, 1783

525 ——— Heloïſe, ou Lettres de Deux Amans, Habitans d'une petite Ville au pied des Alpes, par J. J. Rouſſeau, 4 tom. 12mo. avec fig. ——— Paris, 1764

526 Nouvelles Hiſtoriques, par M. d'Arnaud, 2 tom. 12mo. Maeſtricht, 1782

527 ——— Inſtructions ſur l'Hiſtoire de France à l'Uſage de la Jeuneſſe, par M. Vetour, 1 vol.

528 ——— Obſervations ſur l'Angleterre, par un Voyageur, 12mo. ——— Paris, 1779

529 ——— Vues ſur l'Adminiſtration des Finances et ſur l'allégement de l'Impoſt, par M. de Coubron, 8vo. Haye,

530 Nuits Champêtres de M. de la Veaux, 12mo. Lauſ. 1784

531 La Nuit et le Moment, ou les Matinés de Cythere avec fig. 12mo. ——— Paris, 1764

532 Numa Pompilius, Second Roi de Rome, par M. de Florian, 2 tom. 12mo. fig. ——— Paris, 1786

533 L'Obſervateur François à Londres, ou Lettres ſur l'Etat preſent de l'Angleterre, 6 tom. 12mo. Lond. 1769

534 Obſervations Critiques ſur les Memoires de M. le Baron de Tott, peur ſervir à l'Hiſt. des Turcs et des Tartares, par M. de Peyſſonnel, 12mo. 5 en partie, Maeſtricht, 1785

535 Obſervations Philoſophiques ſur les Principes adoptés par l'Empereur dans les Matieres Eccleſiaſtiques, 8vo. Lond.

536 L'Odyſſée d'Homere traduite en François avec des Remarques, par Madame Dacier, tom. ——— Paris, 1756

537 Oeuvres

537 Oeuvres Choifies de J. J. Rouffeau de Geneve, 15 tom. 12mo. ———— ———— Londres

538 Oeuvres choifies de M. Dorat, 3 tom. 18mo.   Paris, 1786

539 ———— complettes M. de Crebillon, 3 tom. 8vo. ornée de belles Gravures ———— ————   Paris, 1785

540 ————— Complettes de M. Crabillon Fils, 11 tom. 12mo. Maeft. 1779

541 Les Oeuvres Completes de M. de Beaumarchais, contenant fes Memoires, et Pieces Dramatiques, 5 tom. 8vo.   1783

542 Oeuvres Completes de M. Helvetius, 4 tom. 8vo. Lond. 1770

543 ———— completes de M. Marmontel, 11 tom. 8vo. Liege.

544 ————— complettes de M. de Montefquieu, 7 tom. 12mo. Amft. 1784

545 ———— complete de Jean Jaques Rouffeau, 24 tom. 12mo. avec planches ————   Geneve, 1782

546 ————— complettes de M. de Saint Foix, Hiftoriographe des Ordres du Roi, 6 tom. 12mo. ————   Maeft. 1778

547 ————— complettes de Madame de Staal, contenant fes Memoires, et fes Comedies, 2 tom. 12mo.   Maeft. 1783

548 ———— complettes de M. Tiffot, Docteur en Médecine,

549 ———— d'Alexis Piron, 3 tom. 12mo. avec fig.   Paris, 1758

550 ———— de Chirurgie, de M. Goulard, 2 tom. 12mo. Pèzenas et Liege, 1779

551 ———— de Freret, Secretaire de l'Academie des Infcriptions et Belles Lettres, 5 tom. 12mo. ————   Lond. 1787

552 ————— de M. Geffner, traduites de l'Allemand, par M. Huber, 3 tom. 12mo. ornée de fig. ——   Lyon, 1783

553 ———— de Madame la Marquife de Lambert, nouvelle edition, 12mo. ———— ————   Amft. 1766

554 ———— de Madame Riccoboni, 9tom.   12mo.

554 ————— de Jean Racine, 3 tom. 12mo. avec fig. Rouen, 1785

555 ———— de Maitre François Rabelais, publiées fous le titre de Faits et Dits, du Géant Gargantua, et de fon fils Pantagruel, 6 tom. 12mo. avec fig. ————   Amft. 1725

556 ———— de M. Boileau Defpreaux, 2 tom. 12mo. Par. 1778

557 ————— de M. de Boffy, contenant fon Theatre François et Italien, 8 tom. 12mo. ————   Amft. et Berlin, 1768

558 ———— de M. de Crebillon, 2 tom. 12mo.   Paris, 1765

559 ———— de M. de la H****, 3 tom. 8vo.   Yverdon, 1777

560 ———— de M. Greffet, 2 tom. 12mo. ————   Lond. 1765

561 ———— de M. l'Abbé Girard, 2 tom. 12mo.   Leide, 1762

562 ———— de M. l'Abbé de St. Real, 6 tom. 12mo. fig. Amft. 1740

563 ———— de M. Necker, contenant Compte rendu au Roi— Memoire fur l'etabliffemant des Adminiftrations Provinciales, &c. 4to. avec planches ————   Lond. 1785

564 ———— de M. le Grand, Comedien du Roi, 4 tom. 12mo. Paris, 1770

565 ———— de M. Deftouches, 5 tom. 12mo. ornée de belles figures en taille douce ————   Amft. et Leipzig, 1755

566 ————— de Moliere, 6 tom. 12mo. ornée de belles figures en taille douce ————   Amft. et Leipzig, 1765

567 Oeuvres

567 Oeuvres de M. de Montefquieu, 3 tom. 8vo.   Lond. 1777
568 ───── de Montefquieu, 9 vol. 12mo.   Amft. 1785
569 ───── de M. Thomas, de l'Academie Françoife, 4 tom.
8vo. ─────   ─────   Paris, 1773
570 Les Oeuvres de Seneque le Philofophe, traduites en François,
par feu M. La Grange, 6 tom. 12mo.   Paris, 1778
571 ───── de Verfes en Verfe et en Profe, de M. le Chevalier
de Bouflus   ─────   Lond. 1786
572 ───── diverfes en Vers et en Profe, de M. le Chevalier
de B***, 12mo. ─────   Lond. 1786
573 ───── diverfes de Mad. la Comteffe de la Fayette, 2 tom.
12mo. ─────   ─────   Maeft. 1779
574 ───── diverfes de M. de Grecourt, 4 tom. 12mo. avec fig.
Amft. 1772
575 ───── diverfes du Comte Antoine Hamilton, 7 tom. 12mo.
Lond. 1776
576 ───── du Seigneur de Brantome, 15 tom. 12mo. Lon. 1779
577 ───── du Marquis de Villette, 12mo. ─── Lond. 1784
578 ───── (les Chef d') de Deftouches, 3 tom. 12mo. Lieg. 1785
579 ───── Philofophiques de M. Ferret, 8vo.   Loud. 1786
580 ───── mélées de Madame de Prince de Beaumont, 6 tom.
Maeft. 1775
581 Olinde, par l'Auteur des Memoires du Vicompte de Barjac,
2 parties, 12mo. ─────   1784
582 L'Onanifme, Differtation fur les Maladies produites par la
Mafturbation, par M. Tiffot, 12mo.   Laufanne, 1777
583 *Opere del Moliere*, 4 tom. 8vo.   ─────   *Venezia*, 1756
584 *Opere del Sig. Abate Pietro Mataftatio, Poeta Cefares*, 12 tom.
12mo. ─────   *Venezia*, 1781
585 *Opere del Signor Abate Pietro Metaftatio*, 12 tom. 12mo. *Londra.*
586 *Opere di Dazte Alighieri*, 6 tom. 12mo.   *Firenze*, 1774
587 *Opere Filofofiche del Conte Pietro Verri*, 2 tom. 12mo. *Parigi*, 1784
588 Opufcules de M. L**, 8vo.   ───── Berne, 1778
589 Opufcules de Phyfique Animale, et Végétale traduits de
l'Italien de M. l'Abbe Spallanzani, par Jean Senebier,
2 tom. 8vo. fig. ─────   ───── Geneve, 1777
590 *Orlando Furiofo di Lodovico Ariofto*, 4 tom. 12mo. Lond.   1783
591 *Orlando Innamorato di Matteo*, M. *Bojardo rifalto da Francefco
Berni*, 4 tom. ─────   ───── *Parifi*, 1768
592 L'Orphelin Normand, ou les petites Caufes, & les grand
Effets, 4 tom. 12mo.   ───── Paris, 1784
593 La Papeffe Jeanne, Poëme en dix Chants, 8vo. Haye, 1778
594 *Il Poftor Fido del C. Gio. B. Guarini*, 12mo.   *Parigi*, 1782
595 La Payfanne Parvenue, ou les Memoires de Madame la Marquife de L── V──, par M. le Chevalier de Mouhy,
4 tom. 12mo. ─────   ───── Amft. 1777
596 La Payfanne Pervertie, ou les Dangers de la Ville, 4 tom.
12mo. fig. ─────   ───── à la Haye, 1784
597 Le Payfan Parvenu, ou les Memoires de M***, par M. de
Marivaux, 2 tom. 12mo.   ───── Rouen, 1779
598 Penfées de M. le Comte d'Oxenftirn, fur divers Sujets, 2 tom.
12mo. ─────   ───── Paris, 1774
599 **Penfées**

599 Penſées et Reflexions extraites de Paſcal, ſur la Religion, et la Morale, 2 tom. 18mo. —— Paris, 1786

600 Penſées, Maximes, et Reflexions Morales, de François VI. Duc de la Rochefoucault, 12mo. —— Paris, 1777

601 Penſées ſur la Revolution de l'Amerique-Unie, 8vo. Amſt.

602 Le Pere de Famille, Comedie en Proſe, avec un Diſcours ſur la Poeſie Dramatique, par M. Diderot, 12mo. Amſt. 1777

603 Le Petit Magaſin des Enfans ou les Entrenus d'un Pere, 2 vol. 12mo.

604 Le Philoſophe Amoureux, par M. le Marquis d'Argens, 12mo. —— —— à la Haye, 1737

605 Le Philoſophe Anglois, ou Hiſtoire de M. Cleveland, fils Naturel de Cromwel, ecrite par lui-même et traduite de l'Anglois, 8 tom. 12mo. —— Rouen, 1781

606 Philoſophe Parvenu, ou Lettres et Pieces Originales, contenant les Avantures d'Eugene, Sans-Pair, 3 tom. Par. 1787

607 De la Philoſophie de la Nature, ou traité de Morale pour l'Eſpece Humaine, 6 tom. 12mo. —— Lond. 1778

608 Philoſophie de l'Univers, ou Theorie Philoſophique de la Nature, par M. Viallon, 2 parties, 8vo. fig. Brux. 1782

609 Pieces Intéreſſantes, et Peu Connues, pour ſervir à l'Hiſtoire, ou Memorial de M. Declos, Hiſtoriographe de France, 5 tom. 12mo. —— Maeſt. 1781

610 —— Morales et Sentimentales de Madame J. W. Comteſſe de Roſenberg, 12mo. —— Lond. 1785

611 Le Piéd de Fanchette, ou le Soulier Couleur de Roſe, 2 tom. 12mo. —— —— Haye, 1776

612 Les Plaiſirs de l'Amour, ou Recueil de Contes, Hiſtoires, et Poemes Galans, 3 tom. 12mo. fig. Chez Apollon au Mont Parnaſſe —— —— 1782

613 Plinii Caecili Secundi Panegyricus, a Jo. Matthia Geſuero, 12mo. —— —— Gottingae, 1759

614 Poeſies Anciennes, et Modernes, pour ſervir de ſuite, et de Supplement, aux autres Recucils, 2 tom. 12mo. Par. 1781

615 *Poeſie del Signor Abbate Pietro Metaſtatio, Poeta e Bibliotecario Ceſareo, 8 tom. 12mo.* —— *Parigi, 1773*

616 Les Poeſies d'Horace, traduites en François, avec des Remarques, par le R. P. Sanadon, 8 tom. 12mo. Par. 1756

617 —— d'Horace, traduites en Francois, 2 tom. 12mo. Par. 1771, 1772

618 Poeſies de M. le Marquis de la Farre, 12mo. Amſt. 1755

619 —— et Pieces Fugitives diverſes de M. le Chevalier de B***, 8vo. —— —— Paris, 1782

620 Poetique d'Ariſtote, traduite, en François, par M. Dacier, 12mo. —— —— Amſt. 1733

621 Preceptes ſur la Santé des Gens de Guerre, ou Hygienne Militaire, 8vo. —— —— Paris, 1775

622 Precis du Siecle de Louis XV. par M. de Voltaire, 2 parties, 12mo. —— —— Amſt. 1774

623 —— du Siecle de Louis XV. pour ſervir de Supplement à l'Eſſai ſur l'Hiſtoire Générale en 8 vol, et faiſant le tom. 9. 8vo. —— —— Geneve, 1771

624 Precis

624 Precis Hiftorique fur la Vie et les Exploits de François le Fort Général, et Grand Amiral de Ruffie, et Principal Miniftre de Pierre le Grand, Empereur de Mofkovie, par M. de Baffville, 8vo. —— Geneve, 1786

625 Premiere Suite de la Defcription des Experiences Aeroftatiques de M. M. de Montgolfier, &c. avec fig. 8vo. Paris, 1784

626 La Prevention Nationale, 3 tom. 12mo. fig. Haye, 1784

627 *La Prima e la S conda Cena Novelle di Anton Francefco Grazzini, detto Il Lafca,* 12mo. —— *Londra,* 1756

628 Principes du Commerce oppofé au Trafic, developpés, par un Homme d'Etat, 2 tom. 12mo. —— 1787

629 Principes Généraux et Particuliers de la Langue Françoife, par M. de Wailly, 12mo. —— Paris, 1786

630 Principes Généraux et Raifonnés de la Grammaire Françoife, par M. Reftant, 12mo. —— Paris, 1773

631 Principes Philofophiques, Politiques et Moraux, par le Major Weifs, 2 tom. 8vo. —— en Suiffe, 1785

632 Proces de M. de Calonne, ou Replique à fon Libelle, par un Citoyen, 8vo. —— Geneve, 1787

633 Les Provinciales, ou Lettres écrites, par Louis de Montalte, à un Provincial de fes Amis, et aux R. R. P. P. Jefuites, fur la Morale et la Politique de ces Peres, 12mo. 1766

634 Les Pfeaumes de David, mis en Vers François, 12mo. Amft.

635 La Pucelle d'Orleans Poeme, avec des Notes, 12mo. fig. en Swiffe, 1781

636 Queftions fur l'Encyclopédie par des Amateurs, par M. de Voltaire, 9 tom. 8vo. —— 1771

637 La Quinzaine Anglaife, ou Premier et Second Voyages de Mylord de ***, à Paris, 3 tom. 12mo. Yverdon, 1777

638 Recherches Philofophiques fur les Egyptiens, et les Chinois, par M. de P***, 2 tom. 12mo. Amft. et Leyde, 1773

639 —————— Hiftoriques et Politiques fur les Etats-Unis de l'Amerique Septentrionale, par un Citoyen de Verginie, 4 tom. 8vo. —— —— à Colle, 1788

640 —————— fur l'Origine de la Pitié, et divers autres Sujets de Morale, 12mo. —— Lond. 1787

641 Recueil de Pieces Detachées, par Madame Riccoboni, 12mo. Paris, 1772

642 —————— de Voyages Intereffans, pour l'Inftruction, et l'Amufement de la Jeuneffe, par M. Campte, traduit de l'Allemand, tom. 1me, 12mo. Franckfort, 1782

643 —————— des Chef d'Oeuvres, des plus Celebres Beaux Efprit, François, tant en Vers qu'en Profe, 12mo. Edin. 1775

644 —————— des Hiftoires les plus intereffantes, tirées hors de la Bibliotheque de Campagne, 12mo. Bruxelles, 1785

645 —————— des Lettres de Madame la Marquife de Sevigné, à Madame le Comteffe de Grignan fa Fille, 8 tom. 12mo. Paris, 1775

646 —————— des Lettres de Madame la Marquife de Sevigné, à Madame la Comteffe de Grignan, fa fille, 10 tom. 12mo. Maeft. 1783

D 647 Re

647 Recueil des Oraifons Funebres, prononcées par M. Boffuet,
Eveque de Meaux, 12mo. ———— Rouen, 1780
———————————————————— par M. Fléchiér,
Eveque, de Nîmes, 12mo. ———— Rouen, 1783
648 ———— des Oeuvres de Madame du Boccage, 3 tom. 8vo.
Lyons, 1770
649 ———— des Pieces de Théatre lues, par Monf. de Texier en fa
Maifon Lifle Street, Leicefter-fields, 6 tom. 8vo. Lon. 1786
650 Reflexions de l'Empereur Marc-Aurele Antonin, furnommé
la Philofophe, 12mo, ———— Drefden, 1754
651 Reglements de fa Majefté Imperiale Catherine II. pour l'Adminiftration des Governement de l'Empire des Ruffes, traduit de Allemand, 4to. ————— Liege, 1777
652 Reine de Golconde, Conte, par M. D * * *, 8vo.
653 Relation d'un Voyage fait dans l'Intérieur de l'Amerique
Méridionale, depuis la Coté de la Mer du Sud, jufqu'aux
Cotés du Bréfil, et de la Guyane, en defcendant le Riviere
des Amazones, par M. de la Condamine avec une Carte de
la Riviere, 8vo. ————— Maeft. 1782
654 La Religion confiderée comme l'Unique Bafe du Bonheur
et de la Veritable Philofophe, par Mad. la Marquife de Sil-
lery, cidevant Mad. le Comteffe de Genlis, 12mo. Maeft.
655 ————— Poeme, par Monf. Racine, 12mo. Paris, 1777
656 Renaud, Poeme Heroique, imitée du Taffe, par M. Chomorceau,
2 tom. ————— Paris, 1784
657 Les Reveries, ou Memoires fur l'Art de la Guerre, de Maurice
Comte de Saxe, par M. de Bonneville, folio, avec fig.
Haye, 1758
658 La Rhetorique, d'Ariftote, traduite en Francois, par M.
Caffandre, 12mo. ————— Amft. 1732
659 Rhetorique François, par M. Crevier, 2 tom. 12mo. Par. 1767
660 Richard Bodley, ou la Prevoyance Malheureux, par Madame
de Malarme, 2 tom. 12mo. ———— Lond. 1785
661 Richardet, Poeme, 2 parties, 12mo. ———— Liege, 1776
662 La Richeffe da la Hollande, 2 tom. 4to. — Lond. 1778
663 *Le Rime di Francefco Petrarca,* 2 tom. 12mo. *Londra,* 1784
664 Roland l'Amoureux, traduit François, par M. le Sage, 2 tom.
665 Roland Furieux, Poeme Heroique de l'Ariofte, traduction
nouvelle, 2 tom. ————— Amft. 1776
666 Romans, et Contes Philofophiques, par M. de Voltaire,
2 tom. 12mo. ————— Londres, 1775
667 Rouffeau, Juge de Jean Jacques, Dialogue, 12mo. Lichfield,
668 J. J. Rouffeau Juftifié, ou Reponfe à M. Servan, par M.
François Chas, 12mo. ————— Neuchatel, 1780
669 Ruddiman's Livy, Latin, 4 vol. 12mo. ———— Edin. 1772
670 Les Sacrifices de l'Amour, ou Lettres de la Vicomteffe de
Senanges, et du Chevalier de Verfenay, 2 tom. 12mo.
Rouen, 1782
671 De la Sageffes, traduit de l'Anglois, pour fervir de fuite aux
Effais de Montgne, 2 tom. 12mo. ———— Lon. 1769
672 La fainte Bible, par J. F. Oftervald, foh, Laufanne, 1777
673 ———————, par Oftervald, 8vo, Neuchatel, 1771
674 Les

674 Les Saisons, Poeme, l'Abenaki, Sara Th ****, Zimes'
  Contes, 12mo. Amst, 1769
675 Salmon's (Nicholas) Footsteps to the French Language
676 Salmon's (Nicholas) Complete System of the French Language, 8vo. — — Lond. 1788
677 Sandford et Merton, traduction libre de l'Anglois, par M. Berquin, 2 tom. avec fig. — Lond. 1787
678 La Science, et l'Art de l'Equitation, demoutrés d'apres la Nature, par M. du Paty de Clam. 8vo. fig. Yverdon, 1777
679 Secrets concernants les Arts, et Metiers, 2 tom. 12mo. Brux.
680 Sennemourset Rosalie de Civreye Histoire Françoise, 3 tom. 12mo. Amst. 1782
681 Sermons de M. Massillon, Evéque de Clermont, tom. Paris, 1776
682 —— du Pere Bourdalone, de le Compagnie de Jesus, tom. — — Liege, 1784
683 —— pour les Fêtes de l'Eglise Chretienne, pour servir de suite aux Discours sur le Morale Evangelique, par M. Elie Bertrand, 2 tom. 8vo. — Yverdon, 1776
684 —— sur differents Sujets, par le pere Soanen, 2 tom. 12mo. Lyons, 1767
684*Sethos, Histoire ou Vie, tirée des Monuments, Anecdotes de l'Aucienne Egypte, 2 tom. — Paris, 1767
685 Siecle de Louis XIV. et Louis XV. par M. Voltaire, 3 tom. 12mo. — — Neuchatel, 1783
686 Le Spectateur, ou le Socrate Moderne, traduit de l'Anglois, 8 tom. 12mo. avec fig. — Amst. et Leipzig. 1768
  Segevant dedié aux Ames sensible, 2 tom 8vo.
687 Six Nouvelles de M. de Florian, 12mo. fig. Paris, 1786
688 Soirées Provençales, ou Lettres de M. Berenger, 3 tom. 12mo. Paris, 1786
689 Sophie, ou les Amours, et les Malheurs, d'une Fille de Qualitée, 2 tom. 12mo. Amst 1787
690 Supplement à la Bibliotheque Orientale, de M. d'Herbelot, par Messr. Vischelon et Galand, folio 1780
691 —— à l'Histoire Naturelle du Comte de Buffon, 4 tom. 12mo. only 3d. and 4th. vol. Paris, 1776
692 Le Sylphe, traduits de l'Anglois, 2 tom. 12mo. Geneve, 1784
693 Synonimes François, par M. l'Abbé Girard, 2 tom. 12mo. Paris, 1780
694 Systeme de la Nature, ou des Loix du Monde Physique et du Monde Moral, par M. Mirebaud, 2 tom. 8vo. Lond. 1781
695 —— du Monde, par M. Lambert, publié, par M. Marian 8vo, Berlin, Paris, Geneve, 1784
696 Tableau de l'Amour Conjugal, considéré dans l'Etat du Mariage, par M. N. Venette, 2 tom. 12mo. avec fig. 1778
697 Tableau de l'Europe, pour servir de Supplement à l'Histoire, Philosophique et Politique, des Etablissemens et la Commerce, des Européens dans les deux Indes, 8vo. Amst.
698 —— de Paris, 8 tom. 8vo. Amst. 1783
669 —— des Mœurs d'un Siecle Philosophe, Histoire de Justice de St. Val. 2 tom. 12mo. avec fig. — Paris. 1786

700 Tableau des Revolution de l'Empire d'Allemagne depuis Athon le Grand jufqu'à nos Jours, 2 tom.　　　Paris, 1787

701 ———— Tableau Mouvant de Paris, ou Variétés Amufantes, par M. Nougaret, 3 tom. 12mo.　　———　Lond. 1787

702 ———— Natural des Rapport que exiftent entre Dieu, l'Homme, et l'Univers, 2 tom. 8vo.　　—　Edinbourg, 1782

703 Tablettes, Anecdotes et Hiftoriques des Rois de France depuis Pharamond jufqu'à Louis XV. 3 tom. 12mo. Par. 1765

704 Tanzaï et Neaderne, Hiftoire Japonaife, 2 tom. 12mo. Pekin,

705 Telephe, en 12 livres, 8vo.　　———　Lond. 1784

706 Le Temps et la Patience, Conte Moral, par Mad. de Villeneauves, 2 paries,　——　——　Amft. 1768

707 Terées, Tragedie. par M. le Mierre, 8vo.　　Paris, 1787

708 Theatre à l'Ufage des Jeunes Gens, par Mad. le Comteffes de Gens, 4 tom. 12mo.　　———　Paris et Meaft. 1784

709 ———— complete de M. Mercier, 4 tom. avec tres belles figures

710 ————— complete de M. de Voltaire, 11 tom. 12mo. Amft. 1777

711 ———— complete de M. Mercier, 3 tom. 8vo. avec fig. Amft. et Leide, 1778

712 ————— d'Amour. 2 tom. 8vo.　　Cythere et Paris, 1783

713 ————— de Campagne. par l'Auteur des Proverbes Dramatiques,

714 ————— de Pierre Corneille, augmentées de fes Oeuvres diverfes, 6 tom. 12mo. enrichie de figures en tailes douce, Amft. 1740, Amft. et Leipzig, 1765

715 ————— de Thomas Corneille, 5 tom. 12mo. enrichie de fig. en tailles douce,　———　Amft. et Leipzig, 1754

716 ————— de M. de Marivaux, 4 tom. 12mo. Amft. et Leip. 1754

717 ————— de M. de Florian, 3 tom. 12mo. fig.　Paris, 1786

718 ————— pour fervir à l'Education, 4 tom. 12mo.　Faris, 1780

719 ————— de Socété, par l'Auteur du Theatre, à l'Ufage des Jeunes Perfonnes, 2 tom. 12mo.　　Paris, 1781

720 Themidore, 2 paries, 12mo.　———　à la Hague, 1776

721 Therefe Philofophe, ou Memoires pour fervir à l'Hiftoire de D. Dirrag et de Mad. Eradice, 2 parties, 8vo. fig.

722 ————— Philofophe, 2 tom. 12mo. avec fig.　Lond. 1782

723 Le Thevenon. ou les Journées de la Montagne, par M. E. Bertrand, 2 tomo.　　———　Neuchatel, 1777

724 Tiffots Differtatio de Febribus Biliofis, &c. 12mo. Louf. 1780

725 Di Tito Lucrezio Caro della Natura delle Cofe Tradotti la Aleffandro Marchetti, 2 tom.　　———　Londra, 1774

726 Tout eft Poffible à l'Amitie, par Mad. Malarme, 2 parties, Lond. 1786

727 Traduction Libre d'Amedis de Gaule, par M. le Comte de Treff**, 2 tom. 12mo.　　———　Amft. 1780

728 ————————— Nouvelle de l'Art d'Femme d'Ovide Paris, 1784

729 Traite complete d'Anatomie, ou defcription de tout les parties du Corps Humain, par M. Sabbatier, 3 tom. 12mo. Par. 1775

730 ————— de l'Orthographe Francois, en forme de Dictionnaire, par M. Reftaut, 8vo.　———　Poitiers, 1775

731 Traite

731 Traité de la Cateracte avec des Observations, par M. ^e
Wenzel, 8vo. ——— ——— Paris, 1780

732 ——— des Injures dans l'Ordre Judicaire, par M. F. Dareau,
12mo. Paris, 1776

733 ——— du Poeme Epique, par le R. P. le Bossu, 2 tom. 12mo.

734 ——— du Vrai Merite de l'Homme, par M. le Maitro de
de Claville, 2 tom. 12mo. ——— Amst. 1773

735 Le Triomphe de le Nature, Roman Nouveau, 12mo. Amst.
1783

736 Triomphe de l'Intolérance, ou Anecdotes de la Vie d'Am-
broife Borély, mort à Londres, agé de 103 ans. 8vo. Lond.

737 Tufculanes de Cicero, ou traduites en François, par Meffrs.
Bouhier et d'Olivet avec des Remarques, 3 tom. 12mo.
Amst. 1739

738 Une Année de la Vie de Chevalier de Faublas, 7 tom. 12mo.
Lond. 1785

739 Un Petit Mot de Reponfe à M. de Calonne fur fa Requîte au
Roi, par M. Carra, 8vo. —— Amst. 1787

740 De l'Univerfalité de Langue Françoife, 12mo. Berlin, 1785

741 Valentine, ou Lettres et Memoires Intereffans d'une Famille
Angloife, ——— ——— Paris, 1786

742 Le Valife trouve, par M. le Sage, 12mo. avec fig. Mcast. 1779

743 Variétés Morales et Amufantes, tirées des Journeaux Anglois
2 tom. 12mo. ——— ——— Paris, 1784

744 Les Veillées Amufantes, ou Recueil de Nouvelles Hiftoriques,
d'Anecdotes, &c. 6 tom. 12mo. ——— Amst. 1786

745 Les Viellées de Theffalie, par Mad. de Luffen, 2 tom. 12mo.
Paris, 1782

746 Le Vice et la Foibleffe, ou Memoires de deux Provinciales,
2 tom. 12mo. ——— — Lauzanne, 1785

747 Les Veillée du Chateau, ou Cours de Morale, à l'Hiftoire des
Enfans, par l'Auteur d'Adele et Theodore, 3 tom. 12mo.
Paris, 1784

748 Les Veillées de Marais, ou l'Hiftoire du Grande Prince Ori-
beau, Roi de Mommonie, & de le Verteufe Princeffe Ori-
belle, 4 tom. 12mo. ——— Waterford, 1785

749 Vicomte de Bayjac, ou Memoires pour fervir à l'Hiftoire de
ce Siecle, 2 tom. 12mo, ——— Dublin, 1784

750 Vie de Louis Balbe–Berton de Crillon, furnomné le Brave,
et Memoires pour fervir à l'Hiftoire de fon Temps, 12mo.

751 Vie et Lettres de Gellert, traduites de l'Allemend, 3 tom.
8vo. ——— ——— Utrecht, 1775

752 Vies des Hommes Illuftres de Plutarques, par M. Dacier,
15 tom. 12mo. ——— ——— Maest. 1778

753 Vie du Dauphen, pere de Louis XVI. par M. l'Abbé Proyart,
12mo. ——— ——— Paris, 1780

754 *Vita e Azioni dell' Ingegnofo Cittadino D. Chifciotte dell Mancia di
Michel di Cervantes Saavedri, tradotta del Spagnuolo, 4 tom.
8vo.* ——— ——— *Venezie,* 1755

755 Vie et Aventures de Charles Muller Allemand, 8vo.
Cologne, 1786

756 Vie Faibleffe et Repentin d'une Femme, 2 parties, 12mo. 1786

757 La Vie Militaire, Politique, et Privée de Demoifelle D'Eon, ou d'Eon de Beaumont, par M. de la Fortelle, 8vo.
Paris, 1779

758 Vie Privée de Louis XV. ou Principaux Evenemens, Particularités et Anecdotes de fon Regne, 4 tom. orné de Portraits, ——— ——— Lond. 1781
——— Une exemplaire, papier commun, 4 tom. 12mo.
Lond. 1784

759 ——— de M. Turgot, 8vo. ——— ——— Berne, 1787
Vigerius's Greek Dictionary, with Notes, by Hoogeveen 8vo.
Lugduni Batavorum, 1766

760 La Vie Privée du Roi de Pruffe, ou Memoires pour fervir à le Vie de M. de Voltaire, ecrits par lui-même, 18mo. Amft.

761 Vocabulaire François et Italien, extrait de la derniere edition du Dictionnaire de M. l'Abbé Alberti, 2 tom. 8 vo.
à Geneve. 1781

762 Voyages dans les Alpes, précédés d'un Effais fur l'Hiftoire Naturelle des Environs de Geneve, par H. B. de Sauffure, 4 tom. 8vo. fig. ——— Geneve, 1787

763 ————————— précédés d'un Effai fur l'Hiftoire Naturelle de Geneve, par H. B. de Sauffure, 2 tom. 4to.
Neuchatel, 1779

764 Voyage d'Italie & de Hollande, par M. l'Abbé Coyer, 2 tom. 12mo. ——— ——— Paris, 1775

765 ——— de M. de Mayer en Suiffe en 1784, 2 tom. 8vo.
Amft. 1786

766 ——— d'une Suiffe, dans differentes Colonies d'Amerique, pendant la derniere Guerre, avec une table d'Obfervations Meteorologique faites à Saint Dominique, 8 vo. Neu. 1785

797 ——— en Syrie, et en Egypte, pendant les Années 1783, 1784 et 1785, par C. F. Volney, avec cartes et planches, 2 tom. 8vo. ——— ——— Paris, 1787

768 ——— du Lord Henri, Hiftoire Angloife, 12mo. Lond. 1785

769 ——— en Efpagne, par M. le Marquis de Langle, 2 tom. 12mo. Neuchatel, 1785

770 ——— en Pologne, Ruffie, Suede, Dannemarc, &c. par Mr. Wm. Cox, traduit de l'Anglois, par M. P. H, Mallet, orne des Cartes, figures, &c. 4 tom. 8vo. ——— Geneve, 1786

771 ——— par l'Italie, en Egypte, au Mont Liban, et en Paleftine, ou Terre Saint, par M. l'Abbé de Binos, 2 tom. 12mo. ——— ——— Paris, 1785

772 ——— Sentimental en France, 2 tom. 12mo. Paris, 1786

773 ——— du Captaine Robert Lade, en differentes parties de l'Afrique, de l'Afie. et de l'Ameriques, traduit de l'Anglois, 2 tom. 12mo. ——— Paris, 1744

774 Les Vrais Principes du Gouvernement Francois, demontrés, par la Raifon, et par les Faits, 8vo. ——— Geneve, 1777

775 Wather, traduit de l'Allemand, 2 tom. 12mo. Maeft. 1784

776 Zelie dans le Défert, par Madame Daubenton, 2 tom. 8vo.
Geneve, 1787

777 Principes Raifonnés de la Langue Françoife, Ouvrage en Forme d'Amufement, et même de Jeu Scénique, par M. Boulonais, Maitre en Langue Françoife, Angloife, Latine & Grecque.

E N D,

L'ESPRIT

DES

JOURNAUX,

FRANCOIS ET ETRANGERS,

Par une Société de Gens-de-Lettres.

CET Ouvrage périodique, François, dont le succès est décidé depuis plusieurs années, en Europe, ne doit pas être confondu dans la République des Lettres, avec tant d'autres Journaux inutiles, qui n'ont fait que paroître pour être aussi-tôt ensevelis dans un oubli éternel.

Ce Journal, qui paroit tous les mois, contient un précis fidele de ce qu'il y a de meilleur dans les Journaux des autres Nations. Il n'est pas nécessaire de s'étendre sur le mérite d'un Ouvrage, qui est aussi utile aux Arts qu'aux Sciences, & qui tient lieu des autres Journaux, vu qu'il réunit sous un seul point de vue tout ce qui est digne de l'attention du Philosophe & de l'Homme de Lettres.

Les Redacteurs de cet Ouvrage estimable, après avoir extrait des Journaux étrangers tout ce qui peut instruire ou plaire, en présentent les objets sous les divisions suivantes.

I. EXTRAITS. Sous ce titre on fait connoître les Livres François, Italiens, Allemands & Anglois, d'après les Journaux qui en rendent compte; & lorsque, dans des circonstances particulieres, l'importance du sujet l'exige, on en fait une analyse impartiale & séparée, d'après l'Ouvrage même, en s'éloignant également des louanges outrées & de la censure injuste.

II. MELANGES. Ce titre réunit différens morceaux de Littérature, tires des Ouvrages périodiques François & Etrangers, & très-souvent des pieces originales, qui par-là se trouvent sauvées, d'injuste oubli.

III. POESIES FUGITIVES. Cet article contient un choix des meilleures productions des Poëtes François.

L'ESPRIT

DES

JOURNAUX;

Or a Journal of Foreign and English Literature. By a Society of Gentlemen.

THIS periodical publication, in French, whose reputation has been established for a series of years throughout Europe, holds a rank in Letters very different to those numerous Journals, whose inutility have consigned them to immediate and perpetual oblivion.

This work, which appears every month, contains a faithful extract of whatever is valuable in the Journals of other Nations. It is unnecessary to enlarge on the merits of a work no less useful to the Arts and Sciences than to Literature, and which supersedes the necessity of having recourse to similar publications, by collecting under one point of view every thing that appears worthy the attention of the Philosopher and Man of Letters.

The compilers of this valuable performance, after having selected from foreign Journals whatever is instructive or pleasing, arrange the different articles under the following heads.

I. EXTRACTS. Under this article the character of French, Italian, German and English books are given agreeable to their respective Reviews, and, in particular instances, where the magnitude and importance of the subject demands it, an impartial and distinct criticism is given equally distant from fulsome panegyric and unmerited censure.

II. MISCELLANIES. These contain a collection of various Literary extracts from French and other foreign periodical publications, and very frequently original essays, which are by these means preserved from unmerited oblivion.

III. FUGITIVE POETRY. This article contains a selection of the best French Poetry.

III. LITE...

IV. Académies, Societés Littéraires. On indique sous ce titre les sujets & les prix proposés par les différentes Académies de l'Europe.

V. Spectacles. On donne dans cet article une notice impartiale des Pieces de Théatre.

VI. Histoire Naturelle, Physique, Chymie, Botanique.

VII. Medecine, Chirurgie.

VIII. Agriculture, Economie, Industrie, Commerce.

IX. Traits de Bienfaisance, de Justice et d'Humanité.

X. Anecdotes Singularites.

XI. Bibliographie, ou Notice abrégée des Livres de l'Europe.

XII. Gravure.

XIII. Musique.

XIV. Geographie.

XV. Catalogue des Livres Nouveaux.

Tel est le contenu d'un Ouvrage, dont le débit considerable est une preuve assurée de son importance.

L'Esprit des Journaux paroît réguliérement tous les mois ; chaque volume est composé de prés de 500 pages.

Le prix de la souscription est de deux guinées, qu'on doit payer en souscrivant.

On souscrit chez Thomas Hookham, Libraire, New Bond Street, Corner of Bruton Street, à Londres, & chez les différens Libraires des principales Villes d'Angleterre.

Les personnes qui voudront faire annoncer dans l'Esprit des Journaux des Livres, Estampes, Musique, & autres objets, sont priés de les adresser, francs de port, sous enveloppe, à T. Hookham, Libraire, New Bond Street, Corner of Bruton Street.

Chez lequel on trouve aussi tous les Livres nouveaux, instructifs & agréables, en Anglois, Francois, Italien, &c. aussi-tôt qu'ils sont publiés.

IV. Literary Societies. An account of the subjects and prizes proposed by the various Academies throughout Europe.

V. Theatre. Under this article an impartial Review of Dramatic entertainments is given.

VI. Natural Philosophy, Chemistry and Botany.

VII. Physic and Surgery.

VIII. Agriculture, Mechanics and Commerce.

IX. Remarkable Acts of Generosity and Magnanimity, Justice and Humanity.

X. Singular Anecdotes.

XI. A Cataloue, accompanied with an abridged account of the different books as they appear throughout Europe.

XII. Engraving.

XII. Music.

XIV. Geography.

XV. Titles of new Books.

Such are the contents of a publication, whose extensive sale is a decided proof of its importance.

The Esprit des Journaux is published regularly every Month and consists of near 500 pages.

The price to Subscribers is two guineas per annum, to be paid at the time of subscribing.

Subscriptions are taken in by T. Hookham, Bookseller, New Bond Street, Corner of Bruton Street, London, and at the different Booksellers in the principal Towns in England.

Those who wish to have announced in the Esprit des Journaux an account of Books, Prints, Music and other subjects of Science or Literature, are desired to address them, under cover, to T. Hookham, Bookseller, New Bond-street, Corner of Bruton-street.

Where may be had all new Books, on every useful and entertaining subjects, &c. in English, French, Italian, &c. as soon as published.